THE OFFICIAL®
1982
BLACKBOOK
PRICE GUIDE OF
UNITED STATES
PAPER
MONEY
FOURTEENTH EDITION

BY MARC HUDGEONS

COVER PHOTOGRAPH: $100 HAWAIIAN TERRITORIAL NOTE. Issued by the First National Bank of Hawaii at Honolulu Territory, Series of 1882-1908. One of the great rarities of paper currency. Only a single specimen is known to exist. Value $20,000.00.

Published by: The House of Collectibles, Inc.
                 Orlando Central Park
                 1900 Premier Row
                 Orlando, FL 32809
                 Phone: (305) 857-9095

Printed in the United States of America

Library of Congress Catalog Card Number: 80-644107

ISBN: 0-87637-176-4

Y0-AQV-150

TABLE OF CONTENTS

OFFICIAL BOARD OF CONTRIBUTORS

PUBLISHER'S NOTE

The Official Blackbook Price Guide of United States Paper Money is designed as a reference aid for collectors, dealers and the general public. Its purpose is to provide historical and collecting data, as well as current values. Prices are as accurate as possible at the time of going to press but no guarantee is made. We are not dealers; persons wishing to buy or sell paper money, or have it appraised, are advised to consult collector magazines or the telephone directory for addresses of dealers. We are not responsible for typographical errors.

INTRODUCTION

Since its introduction on an emergency basis during the Civil War, paper money has become the cornerstone of American economy — to the point where today's unredeemable notes carry just as much authority as their predecessors, which could be exchanged for gold or silver coins. The urge to collect it is not peculiarly American. The saving and preserving of paper money as historical objects goes back hundreds of years. At no time, however, has such intense collecting enthusiasm gripped the hobby than at present. The number of U.S. collectors, at one period just a handful, has swelled to beyond a million and bids to go much higher. No longer do they accumulate haphazardly but approach the hobby with an almost scientific precision, which would astonish their predecessors of only 40 or 50 years ago. But still there are persons, probably beyond count, who anxiously check each bill that passes into their hands from ordinary circulation, hoping to make a "find." To all of them — the advanced specialist, the investor, the beginner learning about paper money for the first time, the housewife examining supermarket bills — this book is dedicated. If it increases their knowledge, or adds more enjoyment to their endeavors, its goal is attained.

HOW UNITED STATES CURRENCY BEGAN

Paper notes as a substitute for, or adjunct to, metallic money are of extremely early origins. The Chinese are known to have printed the first paper money, in an era contemporary with the European Middle Ages. To say that the western world copied China in issuing paper currency would be mistaken. The technology and apparatus needed to issue such currency were known in Europe as early as the year 1400, but no serious attempts were made in this direction until long afterward. Paper money came to Europe mainly because of financial instabilities, shortage of metal for coinage, or the desire to provide "banking pieces" that would not take huge amounts of coins out of circulation. During the age of colonialism, attempts were made by various local governments in this country to print and circulate paper notes, none of them very successful. There was often a problem of counterfeiting, as simple plates were used that could be reproduced without difficulty, and of building public confidence in this form of money. After establishment of the U.S. mint in 1792, it was confidently believed that America's economic and trade needs could be amply satisfied with coins and no provisions were put forward for paper money, despite the fact that many other nations were using printed currency at that time. Both criticism and approval greeted the government's action. Those in favor of a "coins only" economy argued that the dollar, our chief unit, would be stronger by being represented exclusively by bullion, which even in the event of a change of government or demonetization could be melted down for its metallic content. Others, who at first had shared this view, took up an opposing stand when foreign speculators began to drain away U.S. coinage in the administration of President Jefferson.

Still we did not resort to paper notes in the general issue sense of the term. The nearest this came was in 1815, when the government printed a

3

series of Treasury Notes in various denominations which were in fact promissory notes, or instruments that guaranteed redemption in real money (bullion). They might be called "I.O.U.'s." Those of larger denomination were not designed for public circulation and even the smaller face values did not change hands in any great numbers.

The present series of paper currency had its origins in 1861 and thus is "just" 120 years old. Obviously, modern business could not operate without currency, but very likely its appearance would not even have occurred as early as 1861, without pressing need brought about by the Civil War. Coinage came to be in very short supply almost from the war's outset and both sides, North and South, resorted to printing notes. This was in a sense "emergency money" and at first was disorderly and disorganized. The Union undoubtedly anticipated a return to bullion money as soon as possible upon the war's conclusion. Resumption of regular striking of coins in the mid to late 1860's fell short of meeting the need for money, however, and paper currency continued in use. It in fact increased and has been increasing since. The earliest U.S. notes (1861) are so-called Demand Notes. In 1862 Legal Tender Notes appeared and, subsequently, a variety of others, some of which were in circulation simultaneously.

THE ARTISTRY OF U.S. PAPER MONEY

For the past several decades, our currency has exhibited so few changes of design and design concept that the subject of art in U.S. paper money may seem unprofitable for discussion. The collector is well aware, however, that in the earlier years of currency circulation, especially prior to 1900, much imagination and variety found their way to designs, as well as the use of various colors in printings. Our early notes present a gallery of American engraver's art not to be surpassed in any other medium and are well worthy of collector interest on artistry alone, aside from other considerations.

The regularity and stability of modern designs are a matter of pride to the Treasury Department; they render our currency instantly recognizable in all parts of the world. 19th century designers wished to achieve no such regularity; their pride was in the originality and visual appeal of each new note. Working without rigid guidelines, they shifted portraits, introduced fresh and often unexpected design elements, enlarged or reduced wording, and played endlessly with geometrical shapes and patterns. Much of what they produced could be criticized as overly gaudy by the standards of a later era; but their gaudiness had a motive. The more engraving on a plate, and the more complex that engraving was, the more difficult would be a counterfeiter's task in reproducing the note. Perhaps this explains why U.S. notes of the 19th century were not counterfeited nearly so heavily as those of many other nations, and why counterfeiting subsequently increased. In any case, U.S. notes from the "golden age of design" can be a delight to collect and study. Take a magnifier (a 3X glass is about right), look closely and you're almost sure to notice much that was missed by the eye alone.

Portraits are to be found in abundance on early notes as well as allegorical, mythological and historical scenes. Yes, scenes. Not merely lone figures posing but groups, often comprising numerous components. Some of the most remarkable examples occur on the reverses of the 1863-75 National Bank Notes. True enough, these were Large Size notes, but still the degree of detail is noteworthy. On the $1 denomination is a central medallion depicting the landing of the pilgrims at Plymouth in 1620, as vivid and engaging as presented by any oil rendering. The $5 note has a large oval representation of Columbus landing at San Salvador, occupying about two-thirds the surface area of the note. On the $10 note is a somewhat smaller but no less arresting view of DeSoto on horseback at the Mississippi, entirely faithful to scale and with full background detail. Perhaps the most impressive in the series, and very typical of American studio art at that time (influenced by French romanticism), is the "baptism of Pocahontas" on the $20. No one will argue for the historical accuracy of this subject, but the artwork is splendid and the effect memorable. An extremely complex design on the $50 denomination portrays the embarkation of the pilgrims (bidding farewell to England). This required the accurate portrayal of Stuart costuming and the flair for grand-scale groupings that few artists beyond Rubens and VanDyke possessed.

Other examples of notable designing could be mentioned at length. What nation has ever turned out a note to surpass the $2 Silver Certificate of 1896, with almost the entire obverse taken up by a **borderless** scene in allegory showing "Science" presenting "Steam and Electricity" to "Industry and Commerce"? These are classic types indeed but employed in a fashion in which the Old World never used them. The meaning is, of course, clear enough: steam and electrical power were the two chief contributions of science to industry in the 19th century. On the reverse side were medallion portraits of Robert Fulton and Samuel Morse.

The $5 Silver Certificate of 1896, showing goddess-like figures paying homage to electricity, is a similar theme but handled in an entirely different and creative fashion. For portraiture, it would be difficult to surpass the stalwart Indian Chief shown on the $5 Silver Certificate of 1899.

The 20th century was not totally without commendable designs, but it must be admitted that in the years following World War I their numbers declined. Notes of the 1920's and thereafter must be collected for reasons other than their artwork.

COLLECTING PAPER MONEY

Paper money can be a fascinating hobby. Though of more recent origins than coinage, U.S. paper money exists in enormous varieties and can be collected from many different approaches.

There is much the beginner should learn before doing any serious collecting. This book gives all the information he will need to know about dates, designs, signatures, condition, and, most important, values. Even armed with this knowledge, however, a newcomer to the hobby may be in need of further advice. Where should he buy? Should he build a general or specialized collection? Does paper money have investment potential? How best can he store and care for his collection? What about repairs?

On the whole, general collections are becoming fewer and fewer. Prior to World War II, most paper money enthusiasts were general collectors. Today nearly everyone specializes in one way or another. You cannot **complete** a general collection of U.S. paper money. Furthermore, a general collection containing a bit of this and a bit of that runs the risk of taking on a grab-bag character that will impress neither fellow collectors nor a potential future buyer. The same amount of money that goes into a general collection could, if concentrated upon a particular issue or series, result in a collection from which far greater satisfaction and pride is derived.

There are possible alternatives, if one chooses not to specialize. The most popular of these is "type" collecting — that is, assembling a collection in which one specimen of each different **design** for a certain denomination of note is represented. A type collection could be expanded to cover the whole range of U.S. paper money, but completion of such a collection would be quite expensive.

Potential specialties are numerous. The following is not by any means a complete list.

1. **Series collecting.** Here the collector focuses upon a certain series of notes, such as the $5 1863-75 National Bank Notes, and attempts to collect specimens showing each of the different signature combinations, points of issue, seal colors, or whatever varieties happen to exist in the series. This may sound restrictive but, as an examination of the listings in this book will show, most series comprise a great deal of varieties. Generally, the older the series, the more difficult or expensive will be its completion, while certain series include great rarities beyond the budget range of most of us. The cost can be brought down somewhat if one does not demand the finest condition but is content to own an example of the note in whatever condition he can reasonably afford. (It should be pointed out, though, that in re-selling paper money there is generally a greater loss — or smaller profit — on notes whose condition is less than Very Fine.)

2. **Set collecting.** Sets are groups of notes of different denominations, issued at the same time (or approximately the same time), which were in current circulation together.

3. **Place or origin collecting** — collecting notes by the city whose Federal Reserve Bank issued them.

4. **Signature collecting,** or collecting one specimen of every note bearing the signature of a certain Secretary of the Treasury.

5. **Confederate currency collecting,** the notes issued for use within the Confederate States of America during the Civil War.

6. **Portrait collecting,** by the individual or individuals depicted on the note. This is sometimes known as topical collecting.

7. **Freak and oddity collecting.**

8. **Fractional currency collecting.**

One's imagination, especially if placed into use in a coin-shop well stocked with paper money, will suggest further possibilities. All is fair; there are no strict rules on what makes a worthwhile collection, so long as the material included is not seriously defective or of questionable authenticity.

Don't expect to build a large collection rapidly. Paper money is not comparable to stamps, where a beginner can buy a packet of 1,000/-different stamps and instantly have a sizable collection. Nor should the size of a collection be regarded as a mark of its desirability or worth. Many prize-winning collections contain fewer than a hundred pieces; some consist of only two or three dozen. Direction and quality count much more in this hobby than weight of numbers. He who seeks to own a large collection generally ends up with one whose only recommendation is its size. It may impress beginners but is not likely to be regarded highly by more experienced collectors.

BUYING PAPER MONEY

One of the first questions asked by beginners is: what sort of collection of paper money can be built from bills obtained in ordinary circulation?

Not a very good one, unfortunately. Bills passed in day to day circulation are usually only the most common types, which are of value only in **uncirculated** condition. Hardly any specimens worthy of a collection will reach your hands in this fashion. Occasionally, freak or error notes turn up in circulation, but these instances are so uncommon as to scarcely deserve comment. The serious collector has little choice but to buy in the marketplace. His potential sources of supply include:

1. Dealers.
2. Auction sales.
3. Shows and conventions.
4. Other collectors.

The majority of dealers selling paper money are coin dealers who handle currency as a sideline. This is true of nearly all shops where paper money can be bought. However, if one checks the advertisements in collector magazines he will discover many specialists who trade exclusively in paper money, usually out of their homes or postal box addresses. Their numbers are ever-increasing and they perform an important function for the hobby. Some offer to send selections "on approval," against references or a cash deposit. Others issue price listings describing items in their stock. It should be kept in mind, though, so far as lists are concerned, that the notes offered are often stocked in very limited quantities and some are usually sold out before the list has thoroughly circulated. If the list is not strictly current, there is a good possibility that the prices no longer apply and that you may be billed for additional charges. Before ordering from lists, check the terms or conditions of sale to determine if returns are permitted. Be wary of purchasing from little-known individuals.

Approval selections are a very satisfactory method of buying. Do not order approvals indiscriminately but select a dealer who advertises items within your range of interest and price. Normally you will have ten days to examine selections before making returns. A discount of anywhere from 10 percent to 20 percent, may be offered if you purchase the entire selection.

When returning approval selections, use the same procedure in which they came to you. (If they were sent registered, return them by registered mail).

Browsing in coin shops is the usual way in which beginners get their start buying paper money. Just about every coin dealer — and many stamp dealers — stock paper money to one degree or another, from a single display album with elementary material to vaults filled with literally millions of dollars worth of specimens. Be observant of condition when shopping from dealers' stocks. There is really no excuse for unsatisfactory purchases from shops — the buyer has ample opportunity for inspection. Don't buy in a rush. Get to know the dealer and become familiar with his grading practices. Some dealers will grade a specimen higher than another dealer (but this may be offset by the fact that they charge a lower price).

Bargains. Is it possible to get bargains in buying paper money? To the extent that prices vary somewhat from dealer to dealer, yes. But if you're talking about finding a note worth $100 selling at $50, this is unlikely to happen. The dealers are well aware of market values and the slight price differences that do occur are merely the result of some dealers being overstocked on certain notes or, possibly, having made a very good "buy" from the public. What may appear to be a bargain will generally prove, on closer examination, to be a specimen in undesirable condition, such as a washed bill on which the color has faded.

Auction sales. Many coin auctions feature selections of paper money, and there are occasional sales (mostly of the postal-bid variety) devoted exclusively to it. There is much to be said for auction buying if you have some experience and expertise and know how to read an auction catalogue. In most catalogues, the "book" value of a note is stated without adjustment made for condition. The bidder must make this adjustment himself, based upon the condition as stated in the description or (much better) a personal examination before the sale. If you cannot attend the pre-sale viewing, it may be possible to have certain lots forwarded for your inspection. Unless an item is so scarce that it cannot be found in dealers' stocks, or is offered at auction in a finer grade of condition than dealers can supply, you should not bid the full retail price. Buying at auction for the same price as you can buy at a shop is pointless. On the other hand, bids of 50 percent retail value are generally wasted, as lots seldom sell this cheaply. A logical auction bid is 70-90 percent of the normal dealer price. If you place 10 such bids in a sale, you will probably be successful on about half of them. Of course, much depends on the sale's "glamor." When an important collection is sold it tends to draw higher realizations because the gallery is packed and bidders have come ready and willing to spend large sums of money. Realizations at mail-only auctions are usually, but not invariably, a bit lower than when live bidding is involved. Read the auctioneer's terms of sale carefully before bidding. At some sales, whether you buy in person or by mail, a surcharge of 10 percent is added to the "knockdown" price. This practice — a European importation — is designed as a method of "sharing the cost" of selling between buyer and seller. Instead of charging the seller the usual 20 percent commission, these houses take 10 percent from the seller and 10 percent from the buyer, in the belief that this encourages owners to sell by auction rather than to dealers. It probably does, but it may at the same time discourage **buying** at auction.

Shows and conventions. Paper money is offered for sale at every coin show and exposition. These present excellent opportunities to buy, as the dealers exhibiting at such shows are generally out-of-towners whose stock you would not otherwise have a chance to examine. As many sellers are likely to be offering the same type of material, you have the opportunity to make price and condition comparisons before buying.

Other collectors. The beginner is probably best advised against buying from fellow collectors. This is something of an art as the other party, though not a professional, could well be a talented "haggler" who succeeds in getting more than the true value for his merchandise. Be careful of misrepresentation. A private seller may be entirely honest but could lack the expertise to distinguish a genuine from a counterfeit item. Also, he may have been "struck" with a bad note which he is trying to sell. The private individual, unlike a dealer, has no reputation to guard and is liable to resort to tactics seldom used in the trade. But after you gain sufficient knowledge of paper money, there should be no harm buying from and swapping with fellow collectors, especially persons known to you. Many towns have paper money clubs or coin clubs at which paper money is swapped.

CARE OF YOUR COLLECTION

Paper money is not at all difficult to care for, store and display attractively. It consumes little space and, unlike many other collectors' items, runs no risk of breakage. Nevertheless, it is important that the hobbyist give some attention to its maintenance, as a poorly kept collection soon turns to aimless clutter and provides little enjoyment.

There is not much question but that **albums** are the favorite storage method of nearly all paper money enthusiasts. In the days before specially made albums with vinyl pocket-pages, collectors used ordinary scrapbooks and mounted their specimens with philatelic hinges or photo-corners. This, of course, may still be done if one wishes, but such collections do not have the advantage of displaying both sides of the notes. Furthermore, the use of gummed hinges may be objected to on grounds that they leave marks upon removal, whereas specimens may be removed and reinserted into vinyl-page albums without causing the slightest blemish. We especially recommend the albums and "currency wallet" sold by Anco Coin & Stamp Supply, P. O. Box 782, Florence, Alabama 35630.

Faded color. There is no known restorative for faded color.

Holes. It is suggested that no effort be undertaken to repair holes, as this will almost certainly result in a further reduction in value.

Missing corners. Missing corners can seldom be restored in a manner that is totally satisfactory. The best that can be done is to secure some paper of approximately the same color and texture, trim a small piece to the proper size, and glue it in place as described above. If a portion of printed matter is missing, this can be hand-drawn in ink after restoration. Obviously, this kind of repair is not carried out to "fool" anybody, simply to give a damaged specimen a less objectionable appearance.

Repairs to paper money. Repair work on damaged or defaced paper money is carried out strictly for cosmetic purposes: to improve its physical appearance. Repairs, even if skillfully executed, **will not enhance the value of a specimen**, as it will still be classified as defective. And amateurish repair efforts can very possibly make matters worse.

Tears. Tears can be closed by brushing a very small quantity of clear-drying glue to both sides of the tear, placing the note between sheets of waxed kitchen paper and setting it under a weight to dry. A dictionary of moderate size serves this function well. Allow plenty of drying time and handle gently thereafter.

Wrinkles. Wrinkles, creases and the like can sometimes be improved by wetting the note (in plain water) and drying it between sheets of waxed paper beneath a reasonably heavy weight — five pounds or more. This should not be done with a modern or recent specimen if there is danger of loss of crispness.

Many ills to which paper money falls prey result from not being housed in a suitable album, or any album at all. Framing and mounting presents some risk as the item may then be exposed to long periods of direct sunlight, almost sure to cause fading or "bleaching" of its color.

SELLING YOUR COLLECTION

Few persons beginning a collection of paper money — or anything else — give any thought to the possibility that it will eventually be sold. But this indeed is the fate of every collection, excepting those given to institutions, whether the sale occurs during or after the owner's lifetime. Unfortunately, the careful attention put into assembling a collection is rarely exercised in selling. The sale may be rushed, in order to raise cash quickly; or it may simply be attended to indifferently, because the owner has lost interest in his collection and gone on to other hobbies. Then there is the inherited collection, being sold by a person or persons who played no part in its assembly and know nothing about paper money. In all such instances, the price realized is likely to be lower than could be obtained, had the collection been sold in a proper fashion. There's an art to being a good seller, just as much as being a good buyer. Many persons are embarrassed when selling, or are intimidated by the purchaser. They feel they have no right to question terms offered by an established dealer. Or they simply want to "get it over with." Often, a collector is satisfied getting back 50 percent of the money he put in, in the theory that the remaining 50 percent is the dealer's fair profit. This is erroneous reasoning. If a collection has been years in the building, many of the specimens it contains have probably risen in value and 50 percent of your cost is not a fair offer. Depending on its contents, you may in fact be able to sell at a profit — and still leave plenty of profit for the dealer.

In selling you have the choice of approaching a dealer, auctioneer, or other collectors. The correct choice will be dictated by the type and size of your collection.

Selling to a dealer. All dealers in paper money buy from the public, but not all buy every collection offered to them. Some are specialists and are interested only in collections within their fields of specialization. Some will not purchase (or even examine) collections worth under $100, or $500, or whatever their line of demarcation happens to be. Obviously, a valuable collection containing many hard-to-get notes in VF or UNC condition is easier to interest a dealer in than a beginner-type collection. If a dealer is interested enough to make an offer, this is no guarantee that another dealer would not offer more. In the case of a collection worth $50,000, offers from several dealers might vary by as much as $5,000. This is not an indication that the dealer making the lowest offer is unscrupulous. Dealers will pay as much as the material is worth **to them,** and one dealer may be overstocked on items that another needs badly. Or one dealer may have customers for certain material that another doesn't. For this reason it makes good sense, if you choose to sell to a dealer, to obtain several offers before accepting any. But should you sell to a dealer at all? The chief advantage is quick payment and lack of risk. The price may not be as high as would be obtained at auction, however, depending on the property's nature and pure luck.

Selling by auction. Auction selling presents uncertainties but at the same time offers the possibility of gaining a much better return than could be had by selling to a dealer. It is no easy matter deciding which route to follow. If your collection is better than average, you may be better advised to sell by auction. This will involve a waiting period of, generally, four to six months between consigning the collection and receiving settlement; over the summer months it may be longer. However, some auctioneers will give a cash advance, usually about 25 percent of the sum they believe the material to be worth. In special circumstances a larger advance may be made, or the usual terms and conditions altered. I know of one auctioneer who paid $100,000 under a special contract, stipulating that the money was not to be returned regardless of the sale's outcome or even if no sale took place. But this was on a million-dollar collection. Auctioneers' commissions vary. The normal is 20 percent but some houses take 10 percent from the buyer and 10 percent from the seller. This would appear to work to the seller's advantage, but such a practice may discourage bidding and result in lower sale prices.

Selling to other collectors. Unless the owner is personally acquainted with a large circle of collectors, this will likely involve running ads in periodicals and "playing dealer," which runs into some expense. Unless you offer material at very favorable prices, you are not apt to be as successful with your ads as are the established dealers, who have a reputation and an established clientele.

INVESTING

The great flurry of coin investing and speculation within the past several years has raised the question of whether or not paper money is an attractive or viable target for investment. Certainly it possesses the qualities of a good investment, as the hobby is growing rapidly and retail prices have been increasing steadily. Many notes that could be bought for $100 just five years ago are now in the $500-$1,000 range, while the big rarities bring record price after record price.

The words "investing" and "speculating", often used interchangeably, deserve to be defined. Anything which holds its value over a long period of time, which can be bought without fear of suffering great financial loss when the time comes to sell, may be termed a good investment. Any well-chosen collection of paper money, assembled with care and restricted primarily or exclusively to specimens that are both **popular** and in V.F. or better condition, will appreciate in value, whether bought for the purpose of turning a profit or not. It is often suggested that the best investments are collections not intended for investment, as persons buying for profit often purchase in haste or do not exercise the careful discrimination of a serious collector. They "play the numbers," so to speak, not realizing that the saleability of a collection depends upon more than just its book value. For example, a series collection containing some hard-to-get signature combinations would very likely bring a better price than a few randomly chosen rare notes.

In addition to knowledge of the subject and discretion in buying, time is a necessary ingredient in successful speculation. So, to a degree, is luck, because future movements of the market are never easy to forecast. Even assuming that a particular note increases at a predictable rate, it must be held for a reasonable length of time to pay a satisfactory return. For example, assume that a note is purchased today for $100. Two years from now the same note is selling at retail for $200. It would appear that you've made a sizable profit but there is no profit whatsoever until the item is sold, and for a note priced $200 at retail most dealers will not pay more than about $125. You haven't made $100, the way it looked on paper, but $25 — and considering the "more-than-10 percent-annual" rate of inflation, you've actually lost buying power.

If you decide to speculate in U.S. paper money — which we do not necessarily advocate, but merely provide information for the use of anyone who may be interested — you will probably be more successful following these suggestions:

1. Buy only specimens in V.F. or better condition.

2. Restrict yourself to major issues or varieties rather than items which may be valuable but are so highly specialized that some dealers hesitate to handle them.

3. Do not build a miscellaneous portfolio but concentrate on purchasing specific series or types.

4. Count on waiting at least three years and possibly longer before selling, unless the market experiences a tremendous upsurge. Otherwise the normal pace at which values increase will not allow for a reasonable profit on **most** notes (there are always some exceptions) in less time than this.

5. Beware of bargains. Buy from established dealers or, if sufficiently confident of your abilities, auction houses. If buying for speculation at auction, do not pay more than 70-80 percent of the current retail value.

GLOSSARY

APPRAISALS

Some dealers in paper money undertake appraisal work. They work either for a prearranged fixed fee, or charge a percentage of the collection's value, with a minimum charge of $50 or $100 or more. Choose an appraiser with an established background and determine in advance if a signed certificate of appraisal will be given. If not, the appraiser is not a real professional at this kind of work and his word is likely to carry little weight. In the case of inherited collections that fall into the hands of persons unacquainted with values of paper money, an appraisal prior to sale may be worthwhile.

BROKEN BANK NOTE

Literally, a broken bank note is a note issued by a "broken" bank — a bank that failed and whose obligations could therefore not be redeemed. It may be presumed, by those who recall passing of legislation establishing the Federal Deposit Insurance Corporation, that banks failed only in the financial panic of 1929. During the 19th century, bank failures were common, especially in western and southwestern states. These were generally small organizations set up in frontier towns, which suffered either from mismanagement or a sudden decline in the town's fortunes. Some collectors make a specialty of broken bank notes.

DEMAND NOTES

Demand Notes have the distinction of being the first official circulating paper currency of this country, issued in 1861. There are three denominations: five, 10 and 20 dollars, each bearing its own design on front and back. Demand Notes arose out of the coinage shortage brought about by the Civil War. A total of $60,000,000 in Demand Notes was authorized to be printed, amounting to several million individual specimens. Though this was an extraordinary number for the time, it was small compared to modern output and only a fraction of the total survived. These notes were signed not by any specially designated Treasury Department officers but a battery of employees, each of whom was given authority to sign and affix their names **by hand** in a slow assembly-line process, two signatures to each note. Originally the spaces left blank for signatures were marked "Register of the Treasury" and "Treasurer of the United States." As the persons actually signing occupied neither of these offices they were obliged to perpetually add "for the . . ." to their signatures. In an effort to relieve their tedium, fresh plates were prepared reading "For the Register of the Treasury" and "For the Treasurer of the United States," which required nothing but a signature. This created a rarity status for the earlier specimens, which are now very desirable collectors' items.

ENCASED POSTAGE STAMPS

Though not governmentally issued and not "paper money" in the strict sense of the term, encased postage stamps were made of paper and used as money and therefore have some appeal to currency collectors. This was strictly emergency money to fill the void left by the small change shortage in the Civil War. Many merchants issued their own private tokens, to take the place of pennies in making change. This was not entirely satisfactory to customers, however, who could only redeem such tokens at the place of issue and could suffer losses if the shop closed down. Postage stamps were then resorted to as an alternative. These had full public confidence but presented other problems. After passing from hand to hand, they became wrinkled or grubby or adhered to something and could not be removed without tearing. This was solved by placing the stamps in small metal holders covered with a sheet of transparent mica, allowing them to be handled in the same manner as coins. On the reverse side of the holder appeared the shop's name and, sometimes, an advertising message, though the limited space prevented anything more than a word or two. Not all stamps issued (1¢ to 90¢) were encased. **All encased postage stamps are valuable,** worth a minimum of $100 and a maximum of several thousand dollars depending on denomination and merchant and (sometimes) lettering. With the mica and stamp missing, the impressed containers are of little value. Of course, some of the value of encased postage stamps is accounted for by the scarcity or desirability of the stamps. They are sometimes called "Gault Tokens," after their inventor.

ENGRAVING

Engraving is the process by which designs are printed on U.S. paper money. Engraving involves the use of a metal plate, traditionally copper, into which the design is drawn or scraped with sharply bladed instruments. Ink is smeared over the surface and allowed to work into the grooves or lines comprising the design. The ink is then cleaned away from raised portions (intended to show blank in the printing). The engraving is pressed against a sheet of moistened paper and the ink left in these grooves transfers to the paper resulting in a printed image. When done by modern rotary press, it's a fast-moving process, not much like the engraving work of Albrecht Durer or other Renaissance artists 500 years ago.

FEDERAL RESERVE NOTES

Federal Reserve Notes, the type of notes in current circulation, were authorized by the Federal Reserve Act of December 23, 1913. Issued under control of the Federal Reserve Board, these notes are released through 12 Federal Reserve Banks in various parts of the country. Originally they were redeemable in gold at the United States Treasury or "lawful money" (coins) at a Federal Reserve Bank. In 1934 the option of redemption for gold was removed.

FEDERAL RESERVE BANK NOTES

Federal Reserve Bank Notes were issued briefly in 1915 and 1918. Like National Bank Notes they were secured by bonds or securities placed on deposit by each Federal Reserve Bank with the U.S. government. While issued and redeemable by the member banks of the Federal Reserve system, these notes are secured by — and are obligations of — the government.

FREAK AND ERROR NOTES

Bills which, by virtue of error or accident, are in some respect different from normal specimens. See the section on Freak and Error Notes.

GOLD CERTIFICATES

When gold coinage became a significant medium of exchanges the government decided to hold aside certain quantities of it and issue paper notes redeemable by the Treasury Department. The first Gold Certificates for public circulation were released in 1882. The series lasted until the era of Small Size Currency, ending in 1928. In 1933 all were ordered returned to the Treasury Department for redemption, including those in possession of collectors. A new law in 1964 permitted their ownership by collectors, though they can no longer be redeemed for gold.

LARGE-SIZE CURRENCY

Large-size currency is the term generally used to refer to U.S. notes issued up to 1929, which were somewhat larger in size than those printed subsequently. The increased size permitted more elaborate designing and impressive appearance, which seldom fails to endear Large-Size Currency to beginners. Some of the earlier examples (especially of the 1870's, 1880's and 1890's) are masterworks of art. Though economic considerations were mainly responsible for the switch to a reduced size, there is no doubting that today's notes are far more convenient to handle and carry. They are sometimes referred to as "bedsheet notes."

NATIONAL BANK NOTES

This is the largest group of notes available to the collector. They were issued from 1863 to 1929 and present collecting potential that can only be termed vast. More than 14,000 banks issued notes, in all parts of the country. While the approach to collecting them is usually regional, sets and series can also be built up, virtually without end. The National Banking Act was instituted in 1863, during the Civil War, to permit chartered banks to issue and circulate their own currency. Printing was done at the U.S. Government Printing Office and the designs were all alike, differing only in names of the banks, state seals, bank signatures and the bank's charter number. Each charter bank was limited to issuing currency up to 90 percent of the value of bonds that it kept on deposit with the government. Charters remained in force for 20 years and could be renewed for an additional 20 years. National Bank Notes circulated in the same fashion as conventional currency and, thanks to the bond-deposit system, gained public confidence. The financial panic of 1929, which brought ruin or near-ruin to many banks, put an end to National Bank Notes.

NATIONAL GOLD BANK NOTES

These notes were issued exclusively by California banks during the 1870's under the same terms as ordinary National Bank Notes, their values backed by bonds deposited with the government. Events surrounding their origins form a unique chapter in the history of American economy. Following the discoveries of substantial quantities of gold in California in the late 1840's, that metal soon became the chief medium of local exchange, largely because it was more readily available in that remote region than coinage. Later, when gold coins and tokens began to circulate heavily in California, banks became so swamped with them that they petitioned Washington for authority to issue Gold Notes that could be substituted for the actual coinage. On July 12, 1870, Congress voted favorably on this measure, giving the right to issue such notes to nine banks in California and one in Boston. The Boston bank, Kidder National Gold Bank, appears not to have exercised its right as no Gold Notes of this institution have been recorded. The California banks wasted no time in exercising their authority, the result being a series of notes ranging from five to five hundred dollars in denomination. All were printed on yellow-toned paper so as to be instantly identifiable. The banks issuing these notes were permitted to redeem them in gold coins.

RARITY

Rarity could easily be defined as the degree of difficulty in obtaining a note in the market. But there are many shades and meanings of rarity, some of which have a strong bearing on price and others that influence it hardly at all. In the first place, the exact rarity of most rare specimens — that is, the specific quantity in existence — is not known. And if it were known, a breakdown would need to be made between specimens institutionally owned and not likely to come on the market and those in the hands of dealers and private parties. That rarity seldom serves to establish prices can be demonstrated by the following illustration: Suppose 10 specimens of Note A exist, nine in museums and one coming up at auction. Further suppose that five specimens of Note B exist, all coming up soon for auction. Which do you suppose will draw the heavier bidding on grounds of rarity? Yes, of course, Note A. It's only half so rare as Note B, but buyers tend to think more in terms of what is **left for them** than that which exists as a whole. If a museum buys Note A, its rarity on the market will be absolute — until another is found or a museum decides to sell, which does, as you may know, happen occasionally.

Even if all other circumstances are equal, two notes of equal rarity may be worth vastly different sums. Popularity is a major factor in value.

REFUNDING CERTIFICATES

Refunding Certificates, a sort of hybrid between currency and bonds or securities, were issued under a Congressional Act of February 26, 1879. These were notes with a $10 face value which could be spent and exchanged in the fashion of ordinary money but drew interest at the rate of 4 percent per year. The purposes behind Refunding Certificates were several. They were chiefly designed to encourage saving and thereby curb inflation, which even at that time was becoming a problem. Also, they provided a safe means of saving for persons who distrusted banks (safe so long as the certificates were not lost or stolen), and, probably more important, were readily obtainable in areas of the country not well served by banks. In 1907 the interest was halted. Their redemption value today, with interest, is $21.30.

SERIAL NUMBER

The serial number is the control number placed on all U.S. paper bills, appearing below left-center and above right-center. No two bills in the same series bear repetitive serial numbers. The use of serial numbers is not only an aid in counting and sorting bills as printed but a deterrent to counterfeiting.

SIGNATURES

The inclusion of signatures of Treasury Department officials on our paper bills, a practice as old as our currency (1861), was begun as a mark of authorization and a foil to counterfeiters. The belief was the that handwriting would be more difficult to copy than an engraved designing. Persons whose signatures appear on notes did not always occupy the same office. From 1862 to 1923, the two signers were the Treasurer and the Register (or Registrar as it appears in old writings) of the Treasury. Subsequently, the Treasurer and Secretary of the Treasury were represented. These signatures are of extreme collector importance as some notes are relatively common with certain combinations of signatures and rare with others. A "series" collection is not considered complete until one obtains every existing combination, even though the specimens may be in other respects identical.

SILVER CERTIFICATES

Silver Certificates were authorized in 1878. America's economy was booming at that time and the demand for silver coinage in day to day business transaction outdistanced its supply. Silver Certificates were not intended to replace coinage but to create a convenient medium of exchange, whereby the government held specific quantities of Silver Dollars (later bullion) and agreed to redeem the notes or certificates against them. In 1934 the Treasury Department ceased redemption of these notes in Silver Dollars and on June 24, 1968, redemption in all forms was ended. The notes are still, however, legal tender at their face value. When printing of Silver Certificates was discontinued, a flurry of speculation arose and many persons began hoarding them. This was done not only in hope of eventual redemption for bullion but the belief that such notes would become valuable to collectors. Though Silver Certificates are popular with hobbyists, they have not increased sufficiently in price to yield speculators any great profits — especially since many of the latter were uninformed and saved specimens in less than uncirculated condition.

STAR NOTES

United States Notes, Silver Certificates and Gold Certificates sometimes have a star or asterisk in place of the letter in front of the serial number. Federal Reserve Notes and Federal Reserve Bank Notes have it at the end of the serial number. These notes are known as **"Star Notes"**.

When a note is mutilated or otherwise unfit for issue, it must be replaced. To replace it with a note of the same serial numbers would be impractical, and **"Star"** Notes are therefore substituted. Other than having their own special serial number and a star, these notes are the same as the others. On United States Notes and Silver Certificates, the star is substituted for the prefix letter; on Federal Reserve Notes for the suffix letter. All defective notes are accounted for and destroyed by burning them in an incinerator.

Large stars after the serial number on the 1869 series of United States notes, and 1890 and 1891 Treasury Notes, do not signify replacement notes as are known in later and present day **"Star Notes"**.

Serial numbers on early large size notes were preceded by a letter and were ended by various and curious characters or symbols. These characters are not known to have any significance, except to show that the number was terminated, and prevented any elimination or addition of digits. The suffix characters were replaced by alphabet letters on later issues of notes.

TREASURY OR COIN NOTES

Treasury Notes were authorized by Congress in 1890. Their official title was Coin Notes, as they could be redeemed for silver or gold coins. The series did not prove popular and was discontinued after the issue of 1891.

TREASURY SEAL

The Treasury Seal is the official emblem of the U.S. Treasury Department, which has appeared on all our currency since 1862. It is missing only from the early Demand Notes, issued in 1861, and some Fractional Currency. Two versions have been employed, distinguished readily by the fact that one (the original) bears a Latin inscription, while the current Treasury Seal is worded in English. The basic motif is the same, a badge displaying scales and a key. The original type, somewhat more decorative, was in use until 1968.

UNITED STATES NOTES

Also known as Legal Tender Notes, this substantial and ambitious series followed Demand Notes and constitute the second earliest variety of U.S. paper currency. There are five distinct issues, running from 1862 to 1923.

Though United States Notes are all "large size" and their designs not very similar to those in present use, they show in their successive stages the evolutionary advance from this nation's first efforts at paper money to its currency of today. The first issue is dated March 10, 1862. Denominations are $1, $2, $5, $10, $20, $50, $100, $500, $1,000, $5,000 and $10,000. Individuals portrayed included not only Presidents but other government officials: Salmon P. Chase (Lincoln's Secretary of the Treasury), Daniel Webster, and Lewis and Clark. Some of the reverse designs are masterpieces of geometrical linework. A number of rarities are to be found among Legal Tender Notes, but in general the lower denominations can be collected without great expense.

WILDCAT NOTES

Wild Cat notes are the notes that were issued by so-called "Wildcat Banks," in the era of State Bank Notes (before the Civil War). Numerous banks sprang up around the middle part of the 19th century, mostly in the west and southwest, operated by persons of questionable integrity. Some never had capital backing and were instituted purely as a front for confidence swindles. After issuing notes, the bank shut down, its directors disappeared, and owners of the notes were left with worthless paper. As news traveled slowly in those days, the same persons could move from town to town and work the scheme repeatedly. Notes issued by these banks, or any banks that became insolvent, are also called Broken Bank Notes. Apparently the origin of the term "wildcat" derives from public sentiment of the time, which held that owners of such banks had no greater trustworthiness than a wild animal. "Wildcat" may also refer to the rapid movement of bank officials from one locality to another.

CURRENCY TERMS

Check Letter and Quadrant Number — Federal Reserve District Seal — Serial Number — Treasury Seal — District Numbers — Serial Number — Series — Check Letter and Plate Check Number

THE FEDERAL RESERVE BANKS

The Federal Reserve system is divided into 12 Federal Reserve districts, in each of which is a Federal Reserve Bank. There are also 24 branches. Each district is designated by a number and the corresponding letter of the alphabet. The district numbers, the cities in which the 12 banks are located, and the letter symbols are:

1-A—Boston
2-B—New York
3-C—Philadelphia
4-D—Cleveland

5-E—Richmond
6-F—Atlanta
7-G—Chicago
8-H—St. Louis

9-I—Minneapolis
10-J—Kansas City
11-K—Dallas
12-L—San Francisco

32 SUBJECT SHEET LAYOUT

All United States currency is now printed with 32 subjects (notes) to a large sheet. The first printing is the green back. The second printing is the face of the note in black. This includes the portrait and border, the year or series, the check letter and quadrant number, two signatures and the face plate number. The sheet is then cut in half vertically for the third printing. This includes the black Federal Reserve seal, the four Federal Reserve district numbers, the green Treasury seal and two green serial numbers.

The 32 subject sheet is divided into four quarters called quadrants for numbering and other controls. Each quadrant has its own numbering sequence for the eight notes, with serial numbers advancing by 20,000 to the next note. The quadrant number and check letter in the upper left section indicates the first, second, third or fourth quadrant and the position of the note in the quadrant. In the lower right corner the position letter is shown again with a plate number. On the back of the note the same small number in the lower right is the back plate number.

32 SUBJECT SHEET LAYOUT

	FIRST QUADRANT				THIRD QUADRANT	
A1 A00000001A	A100	E1 A00080001A	E100	A3 A00320001A	A100	E3 A00400001A	E100
B1 A00020001A	B100	F1 A00100001A	F100	B3 A00340001A	B100	F3 A00420001A	F100
C1 A00040001A	C100	G1 A00120001A	G100	C3 A00360001A	C100	G3 A00440001A	G100
D1 A00060001A	D100	H1 A00140001A	H100	D3 A00380001A	D100	H3 A004600001A	H100
A2 A00160001A	A100	E2 A00240001A	E100	A4 A00480001A	A100	E4 A005600001A	E100
B2 A00180001A	B100	F2 A00260001A	F100	B4 A00500001A	B100	F4 A00580001A	F100
C2 A00200001A	C100	G2 A00280001A	G100	C4 A0050001A	C100	G4 A00600001A	G100
D2 A00220001A	D100	H2 A00300001A	H100	D4 A00540001A	D100	H4 A00620001A	H100

SECOND QUADRANT   FOURTH QUADRANT

THE NUMBERING SYSTEM OF UNITED STATES PAPER CURRENCY

The system of numbering paper money must be adequate to accommodate a large volume of notes. For security and accountability purposes, no two notes of any one class, denomination and series may have the same serial number. The two serial numbers on each note have a full complement of eight digits and an alphabetical prefix and suffix letter. When necessary, ciphers are used at the left of the number to make a total of eight digits.

Whenever a numbering sequence is initiated for United States Notes or Silver Certificates, the first note is numbered A 00 000 001 A; the second A 00 000 002 A; the hundredth A 00 000 100 A; the thousandth A 00 001 000 A; and so on through A 99 999 999 A. The suffix letter A will remain the same until a total of 25 groups, or "**blocks**" of 99 999 999 notes are numbered, each group having a different prefix letter of the alphabet from A to Z. The letter "**O**" is omitted, either as a prefix or as a suffix, because of its similarity to zero. The 100,000,000th note in each group will be a star note, since eight digits are the maximum possible in the mechanical operation of numbering machines.

At this point, the suffix letter changes to B for the next 25 groups of 99 999 999 notes, and proceeds in the same manner as the suffix letter A. A total of 62,500,000,000 notes could be numbered before a duplication of serial numbers would occur. However, it has never been required to number that many notes of any one class, denomination and series.

The Federal Reserve Notes printed for the 12 districts are numbered in the same progression as United States Notes and Silver Certificates, except that a specific alphabetical letter identifies a specific Federal Reserve district. The letter identifying each district is used as a prefix letter at the beginning of the serial numbers on all Federal Reserve Notes and does not change. Only the suffix letter changes in the serial numbers on Federal Reserve currency.

PORTRAITS AND BACK DESIGN ON SMALL SIZE NOTES

DENOMINATION	PORTRAIT	BACK DESIGN
$1.00	Washington	Great Seal of the United States
$2.00	Jefferson	Monticello
$5.00	Lincoln	Lincoln Memorial
$10.00	Hamilton	United States Treasury
$20.00	Jackson	The White House
$50.00	Grant	United States Capitol
$100.00	Franklin	Independence Hall
$500.00	McKinley	"FIVE HUNDRED"
$1000.00	Cleveland	"ONE THOUSAND"
$5000.00	Madison	"FIVE THOUSAND"
$10,000.00	Chase	"TEN THOUSAND"
$100,000.00	Wilson	"ONE HUNDRED THOUSAND"

DATING UNITED STATES CURRENCY

Unlike coins, the date is not changed each year on United States Currency.

The date appearing on all notes, large or small size, is that of the year in which the design was first approved or issued. For instance, large size One Dollar United States Notes of the series 1880 were issued with the same date until the new series of 1917 was issued. There was no further date change until the series of 1923.

The same rules apply to small size notes. However, in this case a letter is added after the date to designate or indicate a minor change in the main design or probably a change in one or both of the signatures. For example: the One Dollar Silver Certificate of 1935 was changed to 1935-A because of a change in the size of the tiny plate numbers appearing in the lower right corners of the face and back of the note. It was changed again from 1935-A to 1935-B in 1945 when the signatures of Julian-Morganthau were changed to Julian-Vinson. Subsequent changes in signatures continued the 1935 series to the year 1963 when the signatures of Smith-Dillon terminated the issue with the series of 1935-H. Therefore, these notes were issued for 28 years bearing the date 1935.

NEW TREASURY SEAL

FORMER DESIGN

The former design had the Latin inscription: *"Thesaur. Amer. Septent. Sigil."*, which has several translations. It was the Seal of the North American Treasury.

NEW DESIGN

This new design drops the Latin and states *"The Department of The Treasury 1789"*. First used on the $100 Note of the Series of 1966, as shown below.

GRADES AND CONDITIONS OF PAPER MONEY
CONDITION

The physical condition of a note or bill plays an important role in determining its value. There are many notes that have no premium value (beyond face value) in ordinary condition but are valuable or moderately valuable when uncirculated. Even in the case of scarce early specimens, the price given for an "average" example is generally much less than that commanded by Fine or Very Fine condition. Many 19th century notes that are not hard to get in the usual run of condition are rarities uncirculated. Consequently, when one speaks of rarity, this is always related to the note's condition. There are not too many notes which could be called "rare" in any state of condition.

Currency, being printed on so fragile a substance as paper, is subject to various kinds of damage and wear, and may be found in grades of condition ranging from worthlessly defective to pristine, crisp and apparently never touched by human hands. The older the note, the less it will be likely to retain its crispness, simply due to the effects of old age; but it may still be freshly colored, bright, and without defects, and thereby merit the designation "uncirculated" just as well as a modern note that crackles when handled.

Defects encountered in paper money include:

Creases, Folds, Wrinkles. Generally the characteristic that distinguishes uncirculated notes from those that almost — but not quite — qualify for such designation is a barely noticeable crease running approximately down the center vertically, resulting from the note being folded for insertion into a wallet or billfold. It may be possible, through manipulation or storage beneath a heavy weight, to remove evidence of the crease; but the knowledge that it once existed cannot be obliterated. As a note is passed around from hand to hand the first crease becomes more pronounced and will in time be joined by others, as no two persons are likely to fold it in exactly the same place. It may additionally acquire wrinkles from rough handling in counting, or creases along the corners from being hurriedly thrust into a wallet. As creases and wrinkles increase, the specimen's desirability declines in direct ratio. It soon becomes merely an "average" circulated note, even if no material harm has been suffered. Given enough folding and creasing, especially if it has the luck to come into juvenile hands, it will eventually become "raggy" and limp — at which point nobody, not even the most desperate collector in need of a space-filler, will be very proud to own it.

Discoloration. Discoloration is not as easy to recognize as most defects but it must be classed as one. A distinction should be made between notes printed from under-inked rollers and those which originally were normally colored but became "washed out." Sometimes washing is indeed the cause; a well-intentioned collector will bathe a note, attempting to clean it, with the result that its color is no longer strong. This should not happen if warm (rather than hot) water is used, without strong cleanser. Atmospheric conditions may play some part in discoloration.

Foxing. Fox spots may sometimes be observed on old notes, especially those of the pre-1890 era, just as on old paper in general. They seem more common to foreign currency than American, but their presence on our notes is certainly not rare. These are tiny brownish-red dots, caused by an infestation of lice that attack the paper fibres. Foxing is much more difficult to remove than it appears to be, as the problem is not on the paper's surface.

Holes. Holes are more likely to be encountered in early paper money than specimens of recent origin. In early years it was customary for federal reserve banks to use wire clips in making up bundles of notes for distribution to banking organizations, and these clips or staples often drove their way through the bills. Another common occurrence in grandfather's day was the practice of shop clerks and cashiers in general to impale notes upon holders consisting of nails mounted on stands. Thankfully the cash register reduced and finally eliminated this.

Missing pieces. Missing pieces are a highly undesirable defect which, except in the case of rare specimens, renders the item valueless to collectors. Even if only a blank unprinted corner is torn away, this is called a missing-piece note and hardly anyone will give it a second glance.

Stains. Notes sometimes become stained with ink or other liquids. If the specimen is commonplace and easily obtainable in VF or Uncirculated condition, it will be worthless with any kind of stain. In a note of moderate value, its price will be hurt to a greater or lesser degree depending on the stain's intensity, size, nature, and the area it touches. A stain in an outer margin or at a corner is not so objectionable as one occurring at the center or across a signature or serial number. Ink stains, because of their strong color, are generally deemed the worst, but bad staining can also be caused by oil, crayon, "magic marker" and food substances. Pencil markings, which frequently are found on bank notes, will yield to ordinary erasing with a piece of soft "artgum" worked gently over the surface and brushed away with an artist's camel-hair brush. Most other stains cannot be so easily removed. With ink there is no hope, as any caustic sufficiently strong to remove the ink will also injure the printing and possibly eat through the paper as well. Oil stains can sometimes be lightened, though not removed, by sprinkling the note on both sides (even if the stain shows only on one) with talcum powder or other absorbent powder, placing it between sheets of waxed kitchen paper, and leaving it beneath a heavy weight for several days in a room where the humidity is not unduly high. This treatment might need to be repeated several times and with notes of low value is likely not to be worth all that trouble. Just why persons inscribe their names, slogans, or works of amateur art on money is a question yet to be answered; but when you come into possession of such an example there is little choice but to spend it.

Tears. Tears in notes, very common defect, may be minute or run nearly the whole length of the bill. As a rule the paper on which American currency is printed is fairly rugged and will not tear so readily as most ordinary paper, but given careless or hurried handling anything is possible. An old worn note is more apt to tear in handling than a new one. Repaired tears are more common in the world of paper money collecting than may be generally supposed. A clean tear — that is, one which does not involve loss of surface — can be patched up so as to become virtually unnoticed, unless examined against a light or through a strong glass. X-ray examination will reveal repairs when all else fails.

CONDITION STANDARDS

The following condition standards have been used throughout this book and, with slight variations depending upon individual interpretation, are current generally in the trade. It should, of course, be realized as a fact of life that condition usually appears slightly better than it actually is to a seller, and slightly worse to a buyer.

UNCIRCULATED — UNC. A specimen that for all appearances has not been handled or passed through general circulation; a crisp fresh note in "bank" condition. There may be minor blemishes, such as a finger smudge or pinhole, but if these are in any respect severe the condition merits description as "almost uncirculated." There is not much satisfaction to be taken in a note fresh and crisp that has gaping holes and fingerprints. Obviously, an 1870 "uncirculated" note should not be expected to match a 1970 in appearance or feel. Some respect must be had for age.

ALMOST UNCIRCULATED — A.U. In the case of modern or semi-modern notes, this is generally taken to mean a specimen that shows no evidence of having passed through general circulation but because of some detraction fails to measure up to a rating of "uncirculated." The problem may be finger smudges, counting crinkles, a slight crease, a fold along one or more of the corners, or pinholes. But if more than one of these impairments were present, the item would surely not deserve a classification of "almost uncirculated."

EXTREMELY FINE — X.F. A note exhibiting little evidence of wear from handling, but not so perfect or near-perfect as to qualify for a rating of "uncirculated" or "almost uncirculated." When used of a note issued before 1900 there may be clear evidence of circulation but no disfiguring marks.

VERY FINE — V.F. A very fine note has experienced some circulation but escaped without "being mangled". It is still clean and crisp and its creases are not offensive. It is an entirely presentable specimen for which no apologies need be made, even though its condition is not wholly beyond reproach.

FINE — F. Here the scale begins sliding down. It is obvious that, being the fifth in rank of condition grades, "fine" notes are quite a good deal removed from "uncirculated." They have been handed around pretty thoroughly and suffered the normal consequences, but still are without serious blemishes such as tears, missing corners, serious stains or holes. "Fine" is sometimes referred to as "average circulated," which sounds much worse.

VERY GOOD — V.G. A well-circulated note bearing evidence of much folding, creasing and wrinkling. It may possibly be lightly stained, smudged or pin punctured, but major defects — such as a torn-off corner — would drop it into an even lower category.

GOOD — G. Heavily circulated, worn stamps that are, possibly stained or scribbled on, edges could be frayed or "dog-eared." There may be holes larger than pin punctures, but not on the central portion of design. This is the lowest grade of condition acceptable to a collector, and only when nothing better is available. Unless very rare, such specimens are considered space-fillers only.

A.B.P. — AVERAGE BUYING PRICES

The average buying prices given here are the approximate sums paid by retail dealers for specimens in good condition. As selling prices vary, so do buying prices, and in fact they usually vary a bit more. A dealer overstocked on a certain note is sure to offer less than one who has no specimens on hand. The dealer's location, size of operation and other circumstances will also influence the buying price. We present these figures merely as rough guides.

RECORD KEEPING

For your convenience, we suggest you use the following record-keeping system to note condition of your paper money in the checklist box:

⊠FAIR	⊠VERY GOOD	☐VERY FINE	⊠ALMOST UNC.
☑GOOD	⊟FINE	⊠EXTREMELY FINE	■UNCIRCULATED

ONE DOLLAR NOTES

ORDER OF ISSUE

Face Design: Portrait of Salmon Portland Chase (1808-1873), Secretary of the Treasury under Lincoln, red Treasury Seal, signatures of Chittenden and Spinner, lower right.

Back Design: Large circle center with legal tender obligation.

SERIES SIGNATURES	SEAL	A.B.P.	GOOD	V. FINE	UNC.
1862 Chittenden-Spinner					
☐ Type I-National Bank Note, American Bank Note without Monogram	Red	45.00	75.00	225.00	1300.00
☐ Type II-National Bank Note, American Bank Note with Monogram ABNCO	Red	25.00	45.00	140.00	1200.00
☐ Type III-National Bank Note, National Bank Note without Monogram	Red	25.00	40.00	140.00	1300.00
☐ Type IV-National Bank Note, National Bank Note with Monogram ABNCO	Red	35.00	65.00	175.00	1300.00

ONE DOLLAR NOTES (1869) UNITED STATES NOTES
(ALSO KNOWN AS LEGAL TENDER NOTES)

(Large Size)

Face Design: Portrait of President Washington in the center, large red seal to the right. Scene of Columbus in sight of land, to left, also called "Rainbow Note" because of the many colors used in printing. Black ink for main design, red seal and serial numbers, green background for the serial number, green shading in upper half and blue tint in paper left of portrait to deter counterfeiting.

Back Design: Green, "ONE DOLLAR" and "ONE" over "1" center, letters U. S. interwoven to left. Legal tender obligation to right of center.

SERIES	SIGNATURES	SEAL	A.B.P.	GOOD	V. FINE	UNC.
☐ 1869	Allison-Spinner	Red	40.00	80.00	170.00	1500.00

ONE DOLLAR NOTES (1874-1917) UNITED STATES NOTES
(ALSO KNOWN AS LEGAL TENDER NOTES)

(Large Size)

Face Design: Similar to Note No. 2, no blue or green shading and tinting.

Back Design: Large green "X" with United States of America in the center. Legal tender obligation and counterfeiting warning to right.

SERIES	SIGNATURES	SEAL	A.B.P.	GOOD	V. FINE	UNC.
☐ 1874	Allison-Spinner	Red Sm.	15.00	27.50	125.00	600.00
☐ 1875	Allison-New	Red Sm.	12.00	24.00	80.00	400.00
☐ 1875	Same Series A	Red Sm.	40.00	70.00	400.00	1600.00
☐ 1875	Same Series B	Red Sm.	45.00	85.00	400.00	1600.00
☐ 1875	Same Series C	Red Sm.	82.50	135.00	475.00	1800.00
☐ 1875	Same Series D	Red Sm.	82.50	135.00	500.00	1850.00
☐ 1875	Same Series E	Red Sm.	85.00	140.00	550.00	2150.00
☐ 1875	Allison-Wyman	Red Sm.	12.00	24.00	80.00	400.00
☐ 1878	Allison-Gilfillan	Red Sm.	12.00	25.00	100.00	525.00
☐ 1878	Allison-Gilfillan	Maroon Sm.	—	—	—	2500.00
☐ 1880	Scofield-Gilfillan	Brown Lg.	7.50	15.00	60.00	325.00
☐ 1880	Bruce-Gilfillan	Brown Lg.	12.00	25.00	75.00	360.00
☐ 1880	Bruce-Wyman	Brown Lg.	12.00	25.00	75.00	360.00
☐ 1880	Rosecrans-Huston	Red Lg.	20.00	35.00	250.00	1000.00
☐ 1880	Rosecrans-Huston	Brown Lg.	40.00	75.00	250.00	1100.00
☐ 1880	Rosecrans-Nebeker	Brown Lg.	35.00	60.00	240.00	1100.00
☐ 1880	Rosecrans-Nebeker	Red Sm.	10.00	20.00	60.00	360.00
☐ 1880	Tillman-Morgan	Red Sm.	10.00	17.50	60.00	360.00
☐ 1917	Tehee-Burke	Red Sm.	10.00	12.00	35.00	210.00
☐ 1917	Elliott-Burke	Red Sm.	10.00	12.00	35.00	210.00
☐ 1917*	Burke-Elliott	Red Sm.	20.00	35.00	150.00	450.00
☐ 1917	Elliott-White	Red Sm.	11.00	15.00	35.00	200.00
☐ 1917	Speelman-White	Red Sm.	11.00	15.00	35.00	200.00

Sm.—Small Seal, Lg.—Large Seal

*This note with signatures of Burke and Elliott is an error issue. The regular procedure was to have the signature of the Register of the Treasury on the left, and that of the Treasurer to the right. The signatures were transposed in this instance.

Face Design: Portrait of President Washington in center. Red seal to left, red "1" to the right, red serial numbers.

Back Design: "United States of America" and "ONE DOLLAR" in center. Figures "1" to right and left. This was the last issue of large size "ONE DOLLAR" United States Notes. The last series of large size notes were kept in use until 1929 when the first issue of small size notes were released.

SERIES	SIGNATURES	SEAL	A.B.P.	GOOD	V. FINE	UNC.
☐ 1923	Speelman-White	Red	18.00	25.00	55.00	365.00

ONE DOLLAR NOTES (1928) UNITED STATES NOTES
(ALSO KNOWN AS LEGAL TENDER NOTES)

Face Design: Red seal to left — red serial numbers, large "ONE" to right. This is the only issue of the $1.00 United States Note, small size. At the present time only the $100.00 United States Note is current.

Back Design: Large "ONE" in center with "ONE DOLLAR" overprint, back printed in green.

SERIES	SIGNATURES	SEAL	A.B.P.	GOOD	V. FINE	UNC.
☐ 1928	Woods-Woodin	Red	7.50	11.00	32.00	120.00

Face Design: Name of National Bank top center, maidens at altar below.

Back Design: Landing of Pilgrims—center, state seal of state issuing bank to left eagle and flag.

SERIES	SIGNATURES	SEAL	A.B.P.	GOOD	V. FINE	UNC.
☐Original*	Colby-Spinner	Red w/r	52.50	90.00	375.00	1500.00
☐Original*	Jeffries-Spinner	Red w/r	120.00	300.00	1800.00	7500.00
☐Original*	Allison-Spinner	Red w/r	52.50	90.00	375.00	1500.00
☐1875	Allison-New	Red w/s	50.00	85.00	330.00	1400.00
☐1875	Allison-Wyman	Red w/s	50.00	85.00	330.00	1400.00
☐1875	Allison-Gilfillan	Red w/s	50.00	85.00	330.00	1400.00
☐1875	Scofield-Gilfillan	Red w/s	50.00	85.00	330.00	1400.00

w/r—with Rays, w/s—with Scallops

*Early notes of the First Charter Period did not have the series imprinted on them. They are known by the date on the bill which was usually the date of charter or organization, or as the Original Series. These notes had a seal with rays or small notches. In 1875 the series was imprinted in red and the seal was changed to have scallops around the border. The charter number was added to later issues of notes of the original series and to all notes of the 1875 series.

Face Design:
Portrait of
Martha Washington

Back Design

SERIES	SIGNATURES	SEAL	A.B.P.	GOOD	V. FINE	UNC.
☐1886	Rosecrans-Jordan	Red Sm.	17.50	28.00	135.00	1500.00
☐1886	Rosecrans-Hyatt	Red Sm.	17.50	28.00	135.00	1500.00
☐1886	Rosecrans-Hyatt	Red Lg.	17.50	28.00	135.00	1500.00
☐1886	Rosecrans-Huston	Red Lg.	17.50	28.00	135.00	1500.00
☐1886	Rosecrans-Huston	Brown Lg.	18.00	35.00	150.00	1600.00
☐1886	Rosecrans-Nebeker	Brown Lg.	18.00	35.00	150.00	1600.00
☐1886	Rosecrans-Nebeker	Red Sm.	20.00	39.00	185.00	1800.00

ONE DOLLAR NOTES (1891) SILVER CERTIFICATES
(Large Size)

NOTE NO. 8

Back Design
Face Design:
Same as Note
No. 7.

SERIES	SIGNATURES	SEAL	A.B.P.	GOOD	V. FINE	UNC.
☐1891	Rosecrans-Nebeker	Red Sm.	25.00	40.00	170.00	1400.00
☐1891	Tillman-Morgan	Red Sm.	22.50	32.00	155.00	1300.00

The Educational Note

Face Design: History instructing youth. To the right, panoramic view of the Capitol and Washington Monument. Constitution on tablet, names of famous Americans on top and side borders.

Back Design: Portrait of Martha Washington to left and President Washington to right with large numeral "1" in center.

There is a story that when this note was issued people objected to it because they said, No "1" (ONE) SHOULD STAND BETWEEN GEORGE AND MARTHA WASHINGTON. The set consists of $1.00, $2.00, and $5.00 denominations. They all have very beautiful engravings, and they are truly the most beautiful notes ever issued by our government. They were first released in 1896 and replaced by a new issue in 1899. They were short lived because of objections to the unclad female on the $5.00 note.

SERIES	SIGNATURES	SEAL	A.B.P.	GOOD	V. FINE	UNC.
☐ 1896	Tilman-Morgan	Red	27.50	52.50	220.00	1450.00
☐ 1896	Bruce-Roberts	Red	27.50	52.50	220.00	1450.00

Face Design: Eagle on flag and Capitol background over portraits of Presidents Lincoln and Grant.

Back Design

SERIES	SIGNATURES	SEAL	A.B.P.	GOOD	V. FINE	UNC.
"SERIES OF 1899" is above upper right serial number.						
☐1899	Lyons-Roberts	Blue	8.50	17.00	40.00	300.00
"SERIES OF 1899" is below upper right serial number.						
☐1899	Lyons-Roberts	Blue	10.00	15.00	35.00	275.00
☐1899	Lyons-Treat	Blue	10.00	15.00	35.00	275.00
☐1899	Vernon-Treat	Blue	8.00	12.00	25.00	250.00
☐1899	Vernon-McClung	Blue	8.00	12.00	25.00	250.00
"SERIES OF 1899" is vertical to right of blue seal on the following notes:						
☐1899	Napier-McClung	Blue	8.00	15.00	30.00	275.00
☐1899	Napier-Thompson	Blue	25.00	65.00	500.00	1500.00
☐1899	Parker-Burke	Blue	8.00	15.00	30.00	300.00
☐1899	Teehee-Burke	Blue	8.00	15.00	30.00	275.00
☐1899	Elliott-Burke	Blue	8.00	15.00	30.00	275.00
☐1899	Elliott-White	Blue	8.00	15.00	30.00	275.00
☐1899	Speelman-White	Blue	8.00	15.00	30.00	275.00

Face Design: Portrait of President Washington in center, blue seal left, blue "1 DOLLAR" right, blue numbers.

Back Design: Same as Note No. 4

SERIES	SIGNATURES	SEAL	A.B.P.	GOOD	V. FINE	UNC.
☐ 1923	Speelman-White	Blue	8.00	10.00	20.00	80.00
☐ 1923	Woods-White	Blue	8.00	10.00	20.00	80.00
☐ 1923	Woods-Tate	Blue	15.00	25.00	50.00	210.00

Face Design: Portrait of President Washington, blue seal to the left, "ONE" to right, blue seal and numbers. "ONE SILVER DOLLAR" under portrait.

Back Design

First issue series of 1928. United States paper money was reduced in 1928 from the old large size to the size presently in use. This was mostly an economy measure. Unlike large size notes, the small notes have a letter designation after the date to denote a minor change in design or change of one or both signatures.

SERIES	SIGNATURES	SEAL	A.B.P.	GOOD	V. FINE	UNC.
☐1928	Tate-Mellon	Blue	2.00	4.00	8.00	15.00
☐1928A	Woods-Mellon	Blue	2.00	3.00	6.50	12.00
☐1928B	Woods-Mills	Blue	2.00	3.50	8.00	15.00
☐1928C	Woods-Woodin	Blue	27.50	50.00	100.00	350.00
☐1928D	Julian-Woodin	Blue	27.50	50.00	100.00	250.00
☐1928E	Julian-Morgenthau	Blue	65.00	135.00	350.00	1000.00

ONE DOLLAR NOTES (1934) SILVER CERTIFICATES
(Small Size)

Face Design: Portrait of President Washington, blue "1" to left. "ONE" and blue seal to right. "ONE DOLLAR IN SILVER", under portrait.

Back Design: Same as Note No. 12.

SERIES	SIGNATURES	SEAL	A.B.P.	GOOD	V. FINE	UNC.
☐1934	Julian-Morgenthau	Blue	3.00	4.00	6.00	15.00

ONE DOLLAR NOTES (1935) SILVER CERTIFICATES
(Small Size)

Face Design: Portrait of President Washington in center. Gray "1" to left, blue seal right, and blue numbers. "ONE DOLLAR IN SILVER", under portrait.

SERIES	SIGNATURES	SEAL	A.B.P.	GOOD	V. FINE	UNC.
	The following Notes are Without "IN GOD WE TRUST" on back.					
☐1935	Julian-Morgenthau	Blue	2.00	3.00	8.00	12.50
☐1935A	Julian-Morgenthau	Blue	1.15	2.00	3.50	6.00
☐1935A	Julian-Morgenthau	Brown	4.00	8.00	25.00	60.00

This note was a special issue for use in war zones in the Pacific area during World War II. Brown serial numbers and HAWAII stamped on front and back.

ONE DOLLAR NOTES (1935) SILVER CERTIFICATES
(Small Size)

SERIES	SIGNATURES	SEAL	A.B.P.	GOOD	V. FINE	UNC.
☐1935A	Julian-Morgenthau	Yellow	5.00	10.00	25.00	75.00

The above note was a special issue for use in war zones in the North African and European areas during World War II. Blue serial numbers and yellow seal.

| ☐1935A | Julian-Morgenthau | Blue | 14.00 | 25.00 | 50.00 | 180.00 |

Red "R" between the Treasury Seal and signatures of Morgenthau. This was an experimental issue to test wearing qualities of differently treated paper.

| ☐1935A | Julian-Morgenthau | Blue | 12.00 | 20.00 | 40.00 | 155.00 |

Above note with red "S" between Treasury Seal and signature of Morgenthau. Experimental issue. "R" was for regular paper, "S" for special paper.

☐1935B	Julian-Vinson	Blue	1.15	2.50	4.00	12.00
☐1935C	Julian-Snyder	Blue	1.15	1.50	3.00	4.50
☐1935D	Clark-Snyder	Blue	1.20	3.00	3.75	5.00

Wide design on back. This and all notes of 1935 prior to this, have the wide design. See fig. I.

| ☐1935D | Clark-Snyder | Blue | 1.20 | 1.50 | 2.50 | 4.00 |

Narrow design on back. This and all $1.00 notes following have narrow design. See fig. II.

FIG. I
WIDE
DESIGN

FIG. II.
NARROW
DESIGN
This change was
made during the
1935-D Series.

ONE DOLLAR NOTES (1935) SILVER CERTIFICATES
(Small Size)   NOTE NO. 14

SERIES	SIGNATURES	SEAL	A.B.P.	GOOD	V. FINE	UNC.
☐1935E	Priest-Humphrey	Blue	1.10	1.25	1.50	2.50
☐1935F	Priest-Anderson	Blue	1.10	1.25	1.50	2.50
☐1935G	Smith-Dillon	Blue	1.10	1.25	1.50	2.50

"IN GOD WE TRUST" added. All notes following have the motto.

☐1935G	Smith-Dillon	Blue	1.10	1.25	1.50	3.00
☐1935H	Granahan-Dillon	Blue	1.10	1.25	1.50	2.50

ONE DOLLAR NOTES (1957) SILVER CERTIFICATES
(Small Size)   NOTE NO. 14

The following three notes are the last issue of the $1.00 Silver Certificates. The reason for the change in series from 1935H to 1957 was due to printing improvements. The 1935 series, up until the issue of Clark and Snyder, was printed in sheets of 12 subjects to a sheet. During the term of Clark and Snyder, notes were printed 18 subjects to a sheet. Starting with the series of 1957, new high speed rotary presses were installed and notes were printed 32 subjects to a sheet.

SERIES	SIGNATURES	SEAL	A.B.P.	GOOD	V. FINE	UNC.
☐1957	Priest-Anderson	Blue	1.10	1.25	1.65	2.75
☐1957A	Smith-Dillon	Blue	1.10	1.25	1.65	2.75
☐1957B	Granahan-Dillon	Blue	1.10	1.25	1.65	2.75

The redemption of Silver Certificates by the U.S. Treasury Department ended on June 24, 1968. These notes are now worth only their face value, plus the numismatic value to collectors. Notes in used condition are not regarded as collectors' items.

Face Design: Portrait of Stanton, Secretary of War during the Civil War.

Back Design: Green large ornate "ONE". Entire back is beautifully engraved.

SERIES	SIGNATURES	SEAL	A.B.P.	GOOD	V. FINE	UNC.
☐ 1890	Rosecrans-Huston	Brown	60.00	125.00	450.00	3500.00
☐ 1890	Rosecrans-Nebeker	Brown	60.00	125.00	450.00	3500.00
☐ 1890	Rosecrans-Nebeker	Red	60.00	125.00	450.00	3500.00

Face Design: Is similar to Note No. 15.

Back Design: More unengraved area, numerous "ONE's" and "1's".

SERIES	SIGNATURES	SEAL	A.B.P.	GOOD	V. FINE	UNC.
☐ 1891	Rosecrans-Nebeker	Red	32.50	65.00	175.00	900.00
☐ 1891	Tillman-Morgan	Red	32.50	65.00	175.00	900.00
☐ 1891	Bruce-Roberts	Red	32.50	65.00	175.00	900.00

Face Design: Portrait of President Washington, signature to left of center. Bank and City center, blue seal to right. Signatures of Government Officials above. Signatures of Bank Officials below. Federal Reserve district letter and numbers in four corners.

Back Design: Flying eagle and flag in center. All are series 1918, and have blue seals and blue numbers.

ONE DOLLAR NOTES (1918) FEDERAL RESERVE BANK NOTES
(Large Size)   NOTE NO. 17

BANK & CITY	GOV'T SIGNATURES	BANK SIGNATURES	A.B.P.	GOOD	V. FINE	UNC.
☐Boston	Teehee-Burke	Bullen-Morss ... 6.00	12.00	32.00	225.00
☐Boston	Teehee-Burke	Willet-Morss ... 12.50	25.00	100.00	400.00
☐Boston	Elliot-Burke	Willet-Morss ... 6.00	12.00	32.00	225.00
☐New York	Teehee-Burke	Sailer-Strong.... 6.25	12.50	35.00	225.00
☐New York	Teehee-Burke	Hendricks-Strong 6.25	12.50	35.00	225.00
☐New York	Elliott-Burke	Hendricks-Strong 6.25	12.50	35.00	225.00
☐Philadelphia	Teehee-Burke	Hardt-Passmore .6.00	12.00	32.00	225.00
☐Philadelphia	Teehee-Burke	Dyer-Passmore ..6.50	12.50	35.00	225.00
☐Philadelphia	Elliott-Burke	Dyer-Passmore ..7.50	15.00	40.00	225.00
☐Philadelphia	Elliott-Burke	Dyer-Norris 6.00	12.00	32.00	225.00
☐Cleveland	Teehee-Burke	Baxter-Fancher ..6.00	12.00	35.00	225.00
☐Cleveland	Teehee-Burke	Davis-Fancher ..6.00	12.00	32.00	225.00
☐Cleveland	Elliott-Burke	Davis-Fancher ..6.00	12.00	32.00	225.00
☐Richmond	Teehee-Burke	Keesee-Seay 7.00	14.00	32.00	225.00
☐Richmond	Elliott-Burke	Keesee-Seay 7.00	14.00	32.00	225.00
☐Atlanta	Teehee-Burke	Pike-McCord 6.00	12.00	32.00	225.00
☐Atlanta	Teehee-Burke	Bell-McCord 7.50	15.00	50.00	225.00
☐Atlanta	Teehee-Burke	Bell-Wellborn ... 6.50	12.50	32.00	225.00
☐Atlanta	Elliott-Burke	Bell-Wellborn ... 6.50	12.50	32.00	225.00
☐Chicago	Teehee-Burke	McCloud-McDougal 6.00	12.00	32.00	225.00
☐Chicago	Teehee-Burke	Cramer-McDougal .6.00	12.00	32.00	225.00
☐Chicago	Elliott-Burke	Cramer-McDougal .6.00	12.00	32.00	225.00
☐St. Louis	Teehee-Burke	Attebery-Wells ..7.50	15.00	45.00	250.00
☐St. Louis	Teehee-Burke	Attebery-Biggs ..7.50	15.00	35.00	225.00
☐St. Louis	Elliott-Burke	Attebery-Biggs ..6.50	12.50	35.00	225.00
☐St. Louis	Elliott-Burke	White-Biggs 6.50	12.50	35.00	225.00
☐Minneapolis	Teehee-Burke	Cook-Wold 12.00	20.00	75.00	475.00
☐Minneapolis	Teehee-Burke	Cook-Young ... 50.00	100.00	600.00	2200.00
☐Minneapolis	Elliott-Burke	Cook-Young ... 12.00	20.00	75.00	400.00
☐Kansas City	Teehee-Burke	Anderson-Miller .6.00	12.00	32.00	225.00
☐Kansas City	Elliott-Burke	Anderson-Miller .6.00	12.00	35.00	225.00
☐Kansas City	Elliott-Burke	Helm-Miller 6.00	12.00	32.00	225.00
☐Dallas	Teehee-Burke	Talley-VanZandt .6.50	12.50	35.00	225.00
☐Dallas	Elliott-Burke	Talley-VanZandt 17.50	30.00	125.00	700.00
☐Dallas	Elliott-Burke	Lawder-VanZandt 6.50	12.50	35.00	250.00
☐San Francisco	Teehee-Burke	Clerk-Lynch 6.50	12.50	32.00	225.00
☐San Francisco	Teehee-Burke	Clerk-Calkins ... 6.50	12.50	32.00	225.00
☐San Francisco	Elliott-Burke	Clerk-Calkins ... 6.50	12.50	35.00	250.00
☐San Francisco	Elliott-Burke	Ambrose-Calkins .6.50	12.50	35.00	250.00

Face Design: Portrait of President Washington in center, black Federal reserve seal with city and district letter to left, green Treasury Seal to right. Green serial numbers, Federal Reserve numbers in four corners.

*The note illustrated is the so-called "KENNEDY-DALLAS" note.

Back Design: Same as all $1.00 Notes from 1935.

SERIES OF 1963 GRANAHAN-DILLON — GREEN SEAL

DISTRICT	A.B.P.	UNC.	DISTRICT	A.B.P.	UNC.
☐ 1A Boston	1.30	3.00	☐ 7G Chicago	1.50	3.00
☐ 2B New York	1.50	3.00	☐ 8H St. Louis	1.50	3.00
☐ 3C Philadelphia	1.50	3.00	☐ 9I Minneapolis	1.50	3.00
☐ 4D Cleveland	1.50	3.00	☐10J Kansas City	1.50	3.00
☐ 5E Richmond	1.50	3.00	☐11K Dallas	1.50	3.00
☐ 6F Atlanta	1.50	3.00	☐12L San Francisco	1.50	3.00

*The Dallas note of this series as shown, with the letter "K" in the black seal and the numbers "11" in the four corners does not have any more significance or value than any other notes with their respective district letter and corresponding number.

A false rumor was circulated several years ago that the "K" was for Kennedy, the "11" was for November, the month in which he was assassinated, and that the note was issued by the Dallas bank to commemorate the occasion. The entire story is apocryphal.

This note is in no way associated with the late President Kennedy. The notes were authorized by the act of June 4, 1963. This was five months before Kennedy was assassinated. The Federal Reserve district for Dallas is K-11.

SERIES OF 1963A GRANAHAN-FOWLER — GREEN SEAL

DISTRICT	A.B.P.	UNC.	DISTRICT	A.B.P.	UNC.
☐ 1A Boston	1.25	3.00	☐ 7G Chicago	1.25	3.00
☐ 2B New York	1.25	3.00	☐ 8H St. Louis	1.25	3.00
☐ 3C Philadelphia	1.25	3.00	☐ 9I Minneapolis	1.25	3.00
☐ 4D Cleveland	1.25	3.00	☐10J Kansas City	1.25	3.00
☐ 5E Richmond	1.25	3.00	☐11K Dallas	1.25	3.00
☐ 6F Atlanta	1.25	3.00	☐12L San Francisco	1.25	3.00

ONE DOLLAR NOTES (1963-B) FEDERAL RESERVE
(WITH SIGNATURE OF JOSEPH W. BARR)

(Small Size)   NOTE NO. 18

John W. Barr served as Secretary of the Treasury from December 20th, 1968 to January 20th, 1969, filling the unexpired term of Henry H. Fowler. His signature appears on the $1.00 Federal Reserve notes of the series of 1963-B only.

During the one month term of Joseph W. Barr about 471 million notes were printed with his signature. These notes were for the following Federal Reserve Banks.

NOTES ISSUED

REGULAR NUMBERS		A.B.P.	UNC.	STAR NUMBERS	A.B.P.	UNC.
☐ 2B New York	123,040,000	1.10	3.00	3,680,000	1.20	4.25
☐ 5E Richmond	93,600,000	1.10	3.00	3,040,000	1.20	8.00
☐ 7G Chicago	91,040,000	1.10	3.00	2,400,000	1.20	4.25
☐ 10J Kansas City	44,800,000	1.10	4.00	None Printed		
☐ 12L San Francisco	106,400,000	1.10	3.50	3,040,000	1.20	4.25
	458,880,000			**12,160,000**		

ONE DOLLAR NOTES (1969) FEDERAL RESERVE NOTES
(WORDING IN GREEN TREASURY SEAL CHANGED FROM LATIN TO ENGLISH)

The former design had the Latin inscription: *"Thesaur. Amer. Septent. Sigil.",* which has several translations. It was the Seal of the North American Treasury.

This new design drops the Latin and states *"The Department of The Treasury 1789".* First used on the $100 Note of the Series of 1966.

FORMER DESIGN   NEW DESIGN

ONE DOLLAR NOTES (1969) FEDERAL RESERVE NOTES
(Small Size)

NOTE NO. 18A

SERIES OF 1969—ELSTON-KENNEDY, GREEN SEAL

Boston 2.50	Cleveland 2.50	Chicago 2.50	Kansas City . . . 2.50
New York . . . 2.50	Richmond 2.50	St. Louis 2.50	Dallas 2.50
Philadelphia . . . 2.50	Atlanta 2.50	Minneapolis . . . 2.50	San Francisco . 2.50

SERIES OF 1969A—KABIS-KENNEDY, GREEN SEAL

Boston 2.50	Cleveland 2.50	Chicago 2.50	Kansas City . . . 2.50
New York . . . 2.50	Richmond 2.50	St. Louis 2.50	Dallas 2.50
Philadelphia . . . 2.50	Atlanta 2.50	Minneapolis . . . 2.50	San Francisco . 2.50

SERIES OF 1969B—KABIS-CONNALLY, GREEN SEAL

Boston 2.50	Cleveland 2.50	Chicago 2.50	Kansas City . . . 2.50
New York . . . 2.50	Richmond 2.50	St. Louis 2.50	Dallas 2.50
Philadelphia . . . 2.50	Atlanta 2.50	Minneapolis . . . 2.50	San Francisco . 2.50

SERIES OF 1969C—BANUELOS-CONNALLY, GREEN SEAL

Boston 2.00	Cleveland 2.00	Chicago 2.00	Kansas City . . . 2.00
New York . . . 2.00	Richmond 2.00	St. Louis 2.00	Dallas 2.00
Philadelphia . . . 2.00	Atlanta 2.00	Minneapolis . . . 2.00	San Francisco . 2.00

SERIES OF 1969 D — BANUELOS-SCHULTZ, GREEN SEAL

Boston 2.00	Cleveland 2.00	Chicago 2.00	Kansas City . . . 2.00
New York . . . 2.00	Richmond 2.00	St. Louis 2.00	Dallas 2.00
Philadelphia . . . 2.00	Atlanta 2.00	Minneapolis . . . 2.00	San Francisco . 2.00

SERIES OF 1974—NEFF-SIMON, GREEN SEAL

Boston 1.75	Cleveland 1.75	Chicago 1.75	Kansas City . . . 1.75
New York . . . 1.75	Richmond 1.75	St. Louis 1.75	Dallas 1.75
Philadelphia . . . 1.75	Atlanta 1.75	Minneapolis . . . 1.75	San Francisco . 1.75

SERIES OF 1977—MORTON-BLUMENTHAL, GREEN SEAL

Boston 2.00	Cleveland 2.00	Chicago 2.00	Kansas City . . . 2.00
New York . . . 2.00	Richmond 2.00	St. Louis 2.00	Dallas 2.00
Philadelphia . . . 2.00	Atlanta 2.00	Minneapolis . . . 2.00	San Francisco . 2.00

SERIES OF 1977A-MORTON-MILLER, GREEN SEAL
This series is now in production. All notes are current.

$2.00

TWO DOLLAR NOTES

ORDER OF ISSUE

TWO DOLLAR NOTES (1862) UNITED STATES NOTES
(ALSO KNOWN AS LEGAL TENDER NOTE)

(Large Size)

ALEXANDER HAMILTON (1754-1804)

Face Design: Portrait of Hamilton, cloverleaf twos in upper corners, medallion with "11" in lower left, medallion with "1, 2, 3," right of portrait.

Back Design: "2" in each corner, with "2" motif repeated in scallop circles around obligation, back is printed green.

SERIES	SIGNATURES	SEAL	A.B.P.	GOOD	V. FINE	UNC.
☐ 1862	Chittenden-Spinner					
TYPE I: American Banknote						
Company vertical in left border		Red	40.00	75.00	250.00	1900.00
☐ 1862	Chittenden-Spinner					
TYPE II: National Banknote						
Company vertical in left border		Red	30.00	50.00	200.00	1775.00

TWO DOLLAR NOTES (1869) UNITED STATES NOTES
(ALSO KNOWN AS LEGAL TENDER NOTE)

(Large Size)

Face Design: Portrait of President Jefferson to left, Capitol in center, large red seal to right.

Back Design: Roman II left, Arabic "2" center, "TWO," right. This is the companion note to the $1.00 "RAINBOW NOTE". (see NOTE NO. 2).

SERIES	SIGNATURES	SEAL	A.B.P.	GOOD	V. FINE	UNC.
☐ 1869	Allison-Spinner	Red	32.50	65.00	375.00	2500.00

Face Design:
Portrait of
President Jefferson
same as
previous
Note. No. 20

Back Design: Completely revised.

SERIES	SIGNATURES	SEAL	A.B.P.	GOOD	V. FINE	UNC.
☐1874	Allison-Spinner	Red	40.00	75.00	200.00	1200.00
☐1875	Allison-New	Red	17.50	30.00	100.00	500.00
☐SERIES A	Allison-New	Red	50.00	100.00	225.00	1000.00
☐SERIES B	Allison-New	Red	50.00	100.00	250.00	1100.00
☐1875	Allison-Wyman	Red	17.50	30.00	100.00	500.00
☐1878	Allison-Gilfillan	Red	17.50	32.00	130.00	675.00
☐1878	Scofield-Gilfillan	Red	600.00	1200.00	3000.00	10000.00
☐1880	Scofield-Gilfillan	Brown	14.00	25.00	60.00	325.00
☐1880	Bruce-Gilfillan	Brown	14.00	25.00	60.00	325.00
☐1880	Bruce-Wyman	Brown	14.00	25.00	65.00	375.00
☐1880	Rosecrans-Huston	Red	40.00	75.00	200.00	1200.00
☐1880	Rosecrans-Huston	Brown	25.00	50.00	150.00	1200.00
☐1880	Rosecrans-Nebeker	Red	14.00	25.00	75.00	525.00
☐1880	Tilman-Morgan	Red	12.50	20.00	50.00	375.00
☐1917	Teehee-Burke	Red	9.50	20.00	45.00	275.00
☐1917	Elliott-Burke	Red	9.50	20.00	42.00	225.00
☐1917	Elliott-White	Red	9.50	20.00	42.00	225.00
☐1917	Speelman-White	Red	9.50	20.00	42.00	225.00

TWO DOLLAR NOTES (1928) UNITED STATES NOTES
(ALSO KNOWN AS LEGAL TENDER NOTES)

(Small Size)   **NOTE NO. 22**

Face Design: Portrait of President Jefferson, red seal left, "TWO" right, red serial numbers.

Back Design: Jefferson Home—Monticello.

SERIES	SIGNATURES	SEAL	A.B.P.	GOOD	V. FINE	UNC.
☐1928	Tate-Mellon	Red	5.00	8.50	18.00	65.00
☐1928A	Woods-Mellon	Red	9.00	15.00	40.00	160.00
☐1928B	Woods-Mills	Red	40.00	75.00	150.00	525.00
☐1928C	Julian-Morgenthau	Red	3.00	7.50	18.00	52.50
☐1928D	Julian-Morgenthau	Red	3.00	5.00	10.00	28.00
☐1928E	Julian-Vinson	Red	3.50	7.50	15.00	55.00
☐1928F	Julian-Snyder	Red	3.00	5.00	6.00	25.00
☐1928G	Clark-Snyder	Red	2.75	4.00	5.50	17.50

TWO DOLLAR NOTES (1953) UNITED STATES NOTES
(ALSO KNOWN AS LEGAL TENDER NOTES)

(Small Size)

Face Design: Portrait of President Jefferson, gray "2" to left, red seal to right over "TWO".
Back Design: Same as Note No. 22.

SERIES	SIGNATURES	SEAL	A.B.P.	GOOD	V. FINE	UNC.
☐1953	Priest-Humphrey	Red	2.20	––	4.00	8.00
☐1953A	Priest-Anderson	Red	2.20	––	3.00	7.00
☐1953B	Smith-Dillon	Red	2.20	––	3.00	5.50
☐1953C	Granahan-Dillon	Red	2.20	––	3.00	5.50

Face Design: Same as previous note.
Back Design: "IN GOD WE TRUST" on back.

SERIES	SIGNATURES	SEAL	A.B.P.	GOOD	V. FINE	UNC.
☐1963	Granahan-Dillon	Red	2.20	––	2.60	4.00
☐1963A	Granahan-Fowler	Red	2.20	––	2.60	4.00

Production of Two Dollar United States Notes was discontinued on Aug. 10, 1966.

Face Design: This note is known as "The Lazy Two Note" due to the unusual "lying down" shape of the "2" shown on the face. Liberty with flag and red seal.

Back Design: Sir Walter Raleigh in England, 1585 exhibiting corn and smoking tobacco from America, state seal and eagle.

SERIES	SIGNATURES	SEAL	A.B.P.	GOOD	V. FINE	UNC.
☐Original	Colby-Spinner	Red	100.00	250.00	600.00	3250.00
☐Original	Jeffries-Spinner	Red	500.00	1000.00	2500.00	8000.00
☐Original	Allison-Spinner	Red	100.00	250.00	600.00	3250.00
☐1875	Allison-New	Red	100.00	250.00	600.00	3250.00
☐1875	Allison-Wyman	Red	100.00	250.00	600.00	3250.00
☐1875	Allison-Gilfillan	Red	100.00	250.00	600.00	3250.00
☐1875	Scofield-Gilfillan	Red	100.00	250.00	600.00	3250.00

(Large Size)

Face Design: General Hancock portrait left. Treasury seal to the right of center.

Back Design: "2" left and right, very ornate engraving, obligation in center of Note. Note is printed in green.

SERIES	SIGNATURES	SEAL	A.B.P.	GOOD	V. FINE	UNC.
☐ 1886	Rosecrans-Jordan	Red	37.50	57.50	250.00	2000.00
☐ 1886	Rosecrans-Hyatt	Red Sm.	30.00	55.00	240.00	1850.00
☐ 1886	Rosecrans-Hyatt	Red Lg.	30.00	55.00	240.00	1850.00
☐ 1886	Rosecrans-Huston	Red	30.00	55.00	240.00	1850.00
☐ 1886	Rosecrans-Huston	Brown	37.50	60.00	265.00	2150.00

Face Design: Portrait of William Windom, Secretary of the Treasury 1881-1884 and 1889-1891, red seal right.

Back Design: "2" left and right, scalloped design center with obligation, printed in green.

SERIES	SIGNATURES	SEAL	A.B.P.	GOOD	V. FINE	UNC.
☐1891	Rosecrans-Nebeker	Red	40.00	75.00	400.00	3000.00
☐1891	Tillman-Morgan	Red	40.00	75.00	400.00	3000.00

Face Design: Science presenting Steam and Electricity to Industry and Commerce.

Back Design: Portraits of Robert Fulton and Samuel F. B. Morse.

THIS IS THE SECOND NOTE OF THE POPULAR EDUCATIONAL SERIES

SERIES	SIGNATURES	SEAL	A.B.P.	GOOD	V. FINE	UNC.
☐1896	Tillman-Morgan	Red	55.00	95.00	375.00	4750.00
☐1896	Bruce-Roberts	Red	55.00	95.00	375.00	4750.00

$2.00

Face Design: Portrait of President Washington between figures of Trade and Agriculture, blue "2" left, blue seal right.

Back Design

SERIES	SIGNATURES	SEAL	A.B.P.	GOOD	V. FINE	UNC.
☐ 1899	Lyons-Roberts	Blue	12.50	24.00	85.00	1000.00
☐ 1899	Lyons-Treat	Blue	12.50	24.00	80.00	775.00
☐ 1899	Vernon-Treat	Blue	12.00	22.00	75.00	700.00
☐ 1899	Vernon-McClung	Blue	12.00	22.00	75.00	700.00
☐ 1899	Napier-McClung	Blue	12.00	22.00	75.00	700.00
☐ 1899	Napier-Thompson	Blue	100.00	215.00	350.00	1500.00
☐ 1899	Parker-Burke	Blue	12.50	24.00	85.00	1000.00
☐ 1899	Teehee-Burke	Blue	12.00	22.00	75.00	750.00
☐ 1899	Elliott-Burke	Blue	12.00	22.00	75.00	750.00
☐ 1899	Speelman-White	Blue	12.00	22.00	75.00	750.00

TWO DOLLAR NOTES (1890-1891) TREASURY OR COIN NOTES
(Large Size)

Face Design: Portrait of General James McPherson.

Back Design: Large "TWO" center, over obligation. Large "2" on engraved background right. Intricate engraving, printed green.

SERIES	SIGNATURES	SEAL	A.B.P.	GOOD	V. FINE	UNC.
☐ 1890	Rosecrans-Huston	Brown	60.00	100.00	650.00	4750.00
☐ 1890	Rosecrans-Nebeker	Brown	60.00	100.00	650.00	4750.00
☐ 1890	Rosecrans-Nebeker	Red	60.00	100.00	650.00	4750.00

TWO DOLLAR NOTES (1890-1891) TREASURY OR COIN NOTES
(Large Size)

Face Design: Similar to NOTE NO. 29
Back Design: Revised.

SERIES	SIGNATURES	SEAL	A.B.P.	GOOD	V. FINE	UNC.
☐ 1891	Rosecrans-Nebeker	Red	30.00	65.00	250.00	1200.00
☐ 1891	Tillman-Morgan	Red	30.00	65.00	250.00	1200.00
☐ 1891	Bruce-Roberts	Red	30.00	65.00	250.00	1200.00

$2.00

Face Design: Portrait of President Jefferson to left, name of Bank in center, blue seal to the right, blue numbers, Federal Reserve district letter and number in four corners.

Back Design: American battleship of World War I.

TWO DOLLAR NOTES (1918) FEDERAL RESERVE BANK NOTES

(Large Size)

BANK & CITY	GOV'T SIGNATURES	BANK SIGNATURES	A.B.P.	GOOD	V. FINE	UNC.
☐Boston	Teehee-Burke	Bullen-Morss	15.00	40.00	170.00	700.00
☐Boston	Teehee-Burke	Willet-Morss	15.00	40.00	170.00	700.00
☐Boston	Elliot-Burke	Willet-Morss	15.00	40.00	170.00	700.00
☐New York	Teehee-Burke	Sailer-Strong	15.00	40.00	170.00	700.00
☐New York	Teehee-Burke	Hendricks-Strong	15.00	40.00	170.00	700.00
☐New York	Elliott-Burke	Hendricks-Strong	15.00	40.00	170.00	700.00
☐Philadelphia	Teehee-Burke	Hardt-Passmore	15.00	30.00	115.00	700.00
☐Philadelphia	Teehee-Burke	Dyer-Passmore	15.00	30.00	115.00	700.00
☐Philadelphia	Elliott-Burke	Dyer-Passmore	17.50	35.00	170.00	875.00
☐Philadelphia	Elliott-Burke	Dyer-Norris	15.00	30.00	115.00	700.00
☐Cleveland	Teehee-Burke	Baxter-Fancher	15.00	30.00	115:00	700.00
☐Cleveland	Teehee-Burke	Davis-Fancher	15.00	30.00	115.00	700.00
☐Cleveland	Elliott-Burke	Davis-Fancher	15.00	30.00	115.00	700.00
☐Richmond	Teehee-Burke	Keesee-Seay	17.50	35.00	115.00	750.00
☐Richmond	Elliott-Burke	Keesee-Seay	15.00	30.00	115.00	700.00
☐Atlanta	Teehee-Burke	Pike-McCord	15.00	30.00	115.00	700.00
☐Atlanta	Teehee-Burke	Bell-McCord	27.50	50.00	170.00	800.00
☐Atlanta	Elliott-Burke	Bell-Wellborn	17.50	35.00	115.00	750.00
☐Chicago	Teehee-Burke	McCloud-McDougal	15.00	30.00	115.00	700.00
☐Chicago	Teehee-Burke	Cramer-McDougal	15.00	30.00	115.00	700.00
☐Chicago	Elliott-Burke	Cramer-McDougal	15.00	30.00	115.00	700.00
☐St. Louis	Teehee-Burke	Attebery-Wells	17.50	35.00	115.00	750.00
☐St. Louis	Teehee-Burke	Attebery-Biggs	27.50	50.00	170.00	750.00
☐St. Louis	Elliott-Burke	Attebery-Biggs	27.50	50.00	170.00	750.00
☐St. Louis	Elliott-Burke	White-Biggs	25.00	40.00	170.00	750.00
☐Minneapolis	Teehee-Burke	Cook-Wold	27.50	50.00	170.00	750.00
☐Minneapolis	Elliott-Burke	Cook-Young	27.50	50.00	170.00	750.00
☐Kansas City	Teehee-Burke	Anderson-Miller	25.00	40.00	115.00	750.00
☐Kansas City	Elliott-Burke	Helm-Miller	25.00	45.00	115.00	875.00
☐Dallas	Teehee-Burke	Talley-VanZandt	25.00	45.00	115.00	875.00
☐Dallas	Elliott-Burke	Talley-VanZandt	25.00	45.00	115.00	875.00
☐San Francisco	Teehee-Burke	Clerk-Lynch	25.00	45.00	115.00	875.00
☐San Francisco	Elliott-Burke	Clerk-Calkins	25.00	40.00	115.00	750.00
☐San Francisco	Elliott-Burke	Ambrose-Calkins	25.00	40.00	115.00	750.00

TWO DOLLAR (1976) FEDERAL RESERVE NOTES

(Small Size)

Face Design: Portrait of President Jefferson

Back Design: Signing Of The Declaration of Independence.

SERIES OF 1976 NEFF-SIMON — GREEN SEAL

DISTRICT	A.B.P.	UNC.	DISTRICT	A.B.P.	UNC.
☐ 1A Boston	2.25	4.75	☐ 7G Chicago	2.25	4.75
☐ 2B New York	2.25	4.75	☐ 8H St. Louis	2.25	4.75
☐ 3C Philadelphia	2.25	4.75	☐ 9I Minneapolis	2.25	4.75
☐ 4D Cleveland	2.25	4.75	☐10J Kansas City	2.25	4.75
☐ 5E Richmond	2.25	4.75	☐11K Dallas	2.25	4.75
☐ 6F Atlanta	2.25	4.75	☐12L San Francisco	2.25	4.75

FIVE DOLLAR NOTES

ORDER OF ISSUE

Face Design: Left, Statue of America by Crawford atop United States Capitol. Center, numeral "5" in green. Right, Portrait of Alexander Hamilton, statesman, first Secretary of the Treasury.

Back Design: Numerous small "Fives" in ovals. This note has no Treasury Seal. The signatures are those of Treasury Department employees who signed for the Officials.

PAYABLE AT	A.B.P.	GOOD	V. GOOD
☐Boston (I)	300.00	750.00	1500.00
☐New York (I)	300.00	750.00	1500.00
☐Philadelphia (I)	300.00	750.00	1500.00
☐Cincinnati (I)	300.00	750.00	1500.00
☐St. Louis (I)	300.00	750.00	1500.00
☐Boston (II)	225.00	625.00	900.00
☐New York (II)	225.00	625.00	900.00
☐Philadelphia (II)	225.00	625.00	900.00
☐Cincinnati (II)	225.00	625.00	900.00
☐St. Louis (II)	225.00	625.00	900.00

$5.00

Face Design: Similar to Note No. 32

Back Design:
Note No. 33
First
Obligation

Back Design:
Note No. 33A

Second
Obligation

SERIES	SIGNATURES	SEAL	A.B.P.	GOOD	V. FINE	UNC.
☐ 1862	Crittenden-Spinner*	Red	22.50	37.50	200.00	1450.00
☐ 1862	Crittenden-Spinner**	Red	25.00	40.00	210.00	1550.00
☐ 1863	Crittenden-Spinner**	Red	22.50	37.50	200.00	1450.00

*FIRST OBLIGATION—**SECOND OBLIGATION

FIVE DOLLAR NOTES (1869) UNITED STATES NOTES
(ALSO KNOWN AS LEGAL TENDER NOTE)

(Large Size)

$5.00

Face Design: Portrait of President Jackson on left. Pioneer and family in center.

Back Design: Color, green. This is a companion note to the $1.00 and $2.00 notes of 1869 Rainbow Notes.

SERIES	SIGNATURES	SEAL	A.B.P.	GOOD	V. FINE	UNC.
☐ 1869	Allison-Spinner	Red	27.50	55.00	185.00	1400.00

FIVE DOLLAR NOTES (1875-1907) UNITED STATES
(ALSO KNOWN AS LEGAL TENDER NOTES)

(Large Size)

Face Design: Similar to previous Note.
Back Design: Revised

SERIES	SIGNATURES	SEAL	A.B.P.	GOOD	V. FINE	UNC.
☐1875	Allison-New	Red	17.50	35.00	100.00	450.00
☐1875A	Allison-New	Red	20.00	40.00	120.00	850.00
☐1875B	Allison-New	Red	20.00	40.00	120.00	900.00
☐1875	Allison-Wyman	Red	17.50	35.00	100.00	450.00
☐1878	Allison-Gilfillan	Red	25.00	45.00	120.00	650.00
☐1880	Scofield-Gilfillan	Brown	14.00	40.00	75.00	600.00
☐1880	Bruce-Gilfillan	Brown	14.00	40.00	75.00	600.00
☐1880	Bruce-Wyman	Brown	20.00	40.00	75.00	600.00
☐1880	Bruce-Wyman	Red	14.00	28.00	100.00	500.00
☐1880	Rosecrans-Jordan	Red	15.00	30.00	100.00	550.00
☐1880	Rosecrans-Hyatt	Red	20.00	35.00	200.00	700.00
☐1880	Rosecrans-Huston	Red	30.00	50.00	200.00	750.00
☐1880	Rosecrans-Huston	Brown	14.00	28.00	100.00	600.00
☐1880	Rosecrans-Nebeker	Brown	30.00	50.00	110.00	600.00
☐1880	Rosecrans-Nebeker	Red	14.00	28.00	60.00	400.00
☐1880	Tilman-Morgan	Red	15.00	30.00	60.00	400.00
☐1880	Bruce-Roberts	Red	14.00	28.00	60.00	400.00
☐1880	Lyons-Roberts	Red	14.00	28.00	60.00	400.00
☐1907	Vernon-Treat	Red	8.00	15.00	50.00	300.00
☐1907	Vernon-McClung	Red	8.00	15.00	50.00	300.00
☐1907	Napier-McClung	Red	8.00	15.00	50.00	300.00
☐1907	Napier-Thompson	Red	45.00	75.00	175.00	1000.00
☐1907	Parker-Burke	Red	8.00	15.00	50.00	300.00
☐1907	Teehee-Burke	Red	8.00	15.00	50.00	300.00
☐1907	Elliott-Burke	Red	8.00	15.00	50.00	300.00
☐1907	Elliot-White	Red	8.00	15.00	50.00	300.00
☐1907	Speelman-White	Red	8.00	15.00	50.00	300.00
☐1907	Woods-White	Red	10.00	20.00	50.00	300.00

Face Design: Portrait of President Lincoln center. Red seal to left, red serial numbers.

Back Design: Lincoln Memorial in Washington, D.C.

SERIES	SIGNATURES	SEAL	A.B.P.	GOOD	V. FINE	UNC.
☐ 1928	Woods-Mellon	Red	5.50	8.50	14.00	45.00
☐ 1928A	Woods-Mills	Red	7.50	12.00	23.00	80.00
☐ 1928B	Julian-Morgenthau	Red	5.50	8.75	15.00	37.50
☐ 1928C	Julian-Morgenthau	Red	5.50	8.00	12.00	32.50
☐ 1928D	Julian-Vinson	Red	10.00	15.00	22.50	100.00
☐ 1928E	Julian-Snyder	Red	5.50	7.50	10.00	32.50
☐ 1928F	Clark-Snyder	Red	5.30	7.00	9.50	30.00

FIVE DOLLAR NOTES (1953-1963) UNITED STATES NOTES
(Small Size)

Face Design: Similar to previous note. Portrait of President
Lincoln center. Red seal is moved to the right, red numbers.
Back Design: Similar to previous Note.

SERIES	SIGNATURES	SEAL	A.B.P.	GOOD	V. FINE	UNC.
☐1953	Priest-Humphrey	Red	— —	— —	9.00	25.00
☐1953A	Priest-Anderson	Red	— —	— —	8.50	22.00
☐1953B	Smith-Dillon	Red	— —	— —	8.50	20.00
☐1953C	Granahan-Dillon	Red	— —	— —	8.50	18.00

FIVE DOLLAR NOTES (1953-1963) UNITED STATES NOTES
(ALSO KNOWN AS LEGAL TENDER NOTES)
(Small Size)

SERIES OF 1963

Face Design: Similar to previous Note.
Back Design: The following notes have "IN GOD WE TRUST" on the back.

SERIES	SIGNATURES	SEAL	A.B.P.	GOOD	V. FINE	UNC.
☐1963	Granahan-Dillon	Red	— —	— —	7.00	11.00

Production of Five Dollar United States Notes ended in 1967.

Face Design: The Columbus Note. The face shows Columbus in sight of land and Columbus presenting an Indian Princess.

Back Design: Christopher Columbus landing at San Salvador 1492. Also the State seal left, and American Eagle right.

SERIES	SIGNATURES	SEAL	A.B.P.	GOOD	V. FINE	UNC.
☐Original	Chittenden-Spinner	Red	30.00	100.00	300.00	1200.00
☐Original	Colby-Spinner	Red	30.00	100.00	300.00	1200.00
☐Original	Jeffries-Spinner	Red	150.00	350.00	1250.00	5000.00
☐Original	Allison-Spinner	Red	30.00	100.00	300.00	1200.00
☐1875	Allison-New	Red	30.00	100.00	300.00	1300.00
☐1875	Allison-Wyman	Red	30.00	100.00	300.00	1300.00
☐1875	Allison-Gilfillan	Red	30.00	100.00	300.00	1300.00
☐1875	Scofield-Gilfillan	Red	30.00	100.00	300.00	1300.00
☐1875	Bruce-Gilfillan	Red	30.00	100.00	300.00	1300.00
☐1875	Bruce-Wyman	Red	30.00	100.00	300.00	1300.00
☐1875	Bruce-Jordan	Red		EXTREMELY RARE		
☐1875	Rosecrans-Huston	Red	30.00	100.00	300.00	1300.00
☐1875	Rosecrans-Jordan	Red	30.00	100.00	300.00	1300.00

First Issue — brown seal and brown backs.

Face Design: Portrait of President Garfield left. Name of Bank and City center, brown seal to right. Brown charter number.

Back Design: Brown border-design similar to previous note. Center oval now has the Bank's charter number in green. The top signatures are those of the Treasury Officials. Bottom signatures, usually hand written or probably rubber stamped, are Bank Officials.

SERIES	SIGNATURES	SEAL	A.B.P.	GOOD	V. FINE	UNC.
☐1882	Bruce-Gilfillan	Brown	27.50	50.00	110.00	585.00
☐1882	Bruce-Wyman	Brown	27.50	50.00	110.00	585.00
☐1882	Bruce-Jordan	Brown	27.50	50.00	110.00	585.00
☐1882	Rosecrans-Jordan	Brown	27.50	50.00	110.00	585.00
☐1882	Rosecrans-Hyatt	Brown	27.50	50.00	110.00	585.00
☐1882	Rosecrans-Huston	Brown	27.50	50.00	110.00	585.00
☐1882	Rosecrans-Nebeker	Brown	27.50	50.00	110.00	585.00
☐1882	Rosecrans-Morgan	Brown	135.00	225.00	975.00	2000.00
☐1882	Tillman-Morgan	Brown	27.50	50.00	110.00	585.00
☐1882	Tillman-Roberts	Brown	27.50	50.00	110.00	585.00
☐1882	Bruce-Roberts	Brown	27.50	50.00	110.00	585.00
☐1882	Lyons-Roberts	Brown	27.50	50.00	110.00	585.00
☐1882	Lyons-Treat (Unknown in any collection)					
☐1882	Vernon-Treat	Brown	28.50	55.00	220.00	700.00

Face Design: Similar to preceding portrait of President Garfield.

Back Design: Back is now green with date 1882-1908 in center.

SERIES	SIGNATURES	SEAL	A.B.P.	GOOD	V. FINE	UNC.
☐1882	Rosecrans-Huston	Blue	14.00	30.00	125.00	850.00
☐1882	Rosecrans-Nebeker	Blue	14.00	30.00	125.00	850.00
☐1882	Rosecrans-Morgan	Blue	110.00	250.00	850.00	3500.00
☐1882	Tillman-Morgan	Blue	14.00	30.00	125.00	850.00
☐1882	Tillman-Roberts	Blue	22.50	45.00	125.00	850.00
☐1882	Bruce-Roberts	Blue	14.00	30.00	125.00	850.00
☐1882	Lyons-Roberts	Blue	14.00	30.00	125.00	850.00
☐1882	Vernon-Treat	Blue	14.00	30.00	125.00	850.00
☐1882	Vernon-McClung	RARE				
☐1882	Napier-McClung	RARE				

Face Design: Same as Note No. 39. Blue Seal.

Back Design: Similar to Note No. 40, "FIVE DOLLARS" replaces 1882-1908.

SERIES	SIGNATURES	SEAL	A.B.P.	GOOD	V. FINE	UNC.
☐ 1882	Tillman-Morgan	Blue	22.50	60.00	325.00	1750.00
☐ 1882	Tillman-Roberts	Blue	90.00	165.00	650.00	2500.00
☐ 1882	Bruce-Roberts	Blue	90.00	165.00	650.00	2500.00
☐ 1882	Lyons-Roberts	Blue	22.50	60.00	325.00	1750.00
☐ 1882	Vernon-Treat	Blue	32.50	110.00	430.00	1750.00
☐ 1882	Napier-McClung	Blue	32.50	110.00	430.00	1750.00
☐ 1882	Teehee-Burke	Blue		EXTREMELY RARE		

$5.00

First Issue— red seal and charter numbers.
Face Design: Portrait of President Harrison left, name of Bank and City center, Treasury Seal to right, red seal and Charter number.

Back Design: Landing of Pilgrims.

SERIES	SIGNATURES	SEAL	A.B.P.	GOOD	V. FINE	UNC.
☐1902	Lyons-Roberts	Red	22.00	45.00	110.00	650.00
☐1902	Lyons-Treat	Red	25.00	57.50	165.00	700.00
☐1902	Vernon-Treat	Red	28.00	80.00	195.00	750.00

Second Issue — seal, Charter numbers and serial numbers are now changed to blue, back of note now has 1902-1908 added.

SERIES	SIGNATURES	SEAL	A.B.P.	GOOD	V. FINE	UNC.
☐1902	Lyons-Roberts	Blue	11.00	18.00	37.50	285.00
☐1902	Lyons-Treat	Blue	11.00	18.00	37.50	285.00
☐1902	Vernon-Treat	Blue	11.00	18.00	37.50	285.00
☐1902	Vernon-McClung	Blue	11.00	18.00	37.50	285.00
☐1902	Napier-McClung	Blue	11.00	18.00	37.50	285.00
☐1902	Napier-Thompson	Blue	22.00	32.00	125.00	650.00
☐1902	Napier-Burke	Blue	11.00	18.00	37.50	285.00
☐1902	Parker-Burke	Blue	11.00	18.00	37.50	285.00
☐1902	Teehee-Burke	Blue	27.50	42.50	135.00	800.00

Third Issue — blue seal and numbers. The following Notes do not have date of 1902-1908 on the back.

SERIES	SIGNATURES	SEAL	A.B.P.	GOOD	V. FINE	UNC.
☐1902	Lyons-Roberts	Blue	9.00	15.00	27.00	265.00
☐1902	Lyons-Treat	Blue	9.00	15.00	27.00	265.00
☐1902	Vernon-Treat	Blue	9.00	15.00	27.00	265.00
☐1902	Vernon-McClung	Blue	9.00	15.00	27.00	265.00
☐1902	Napier-McClung	Blue	9.00	15.00	27.00	265.00
☐1902	Napier-Thompson	Blue	14.00	22.00	60.00	395.00
☐1902	Napier-Burke	Blue	9.00	15.00	27.00	265.00
☐1902	Parker-Burke	Blue	9.00	15.00	27.00	265.00
☐1902	Teehee-Burke	Blue	9.00	15.00	27.00	265.00
☐1902	Elliott-Burke	Blue	9.00	15.00	27.00	265.00
☐1902	Elliott-White	Blue	9.00	15.00	27.00	265.00
☐1902	Speelman-White	Blue	9.00	15.00	27.00	265.00
☐1902	Woods-White	Blue	9.00	15.00	27.00	265.00
☐1902	Woods-Tate	Blue	14.00	22.00	60.00	395.00
☐1902	Jones-Wood	Blue	55.00	110.00	300.00	2500.00

FIVE DOLLAR NOTES (1929) NATIONAL BANK NOTES
(Small Size)

TYPE I

TYPE II

Face Design: Portrait of President Lincoln in center, name of Bank to left, brown seal to the right. TYPE I — Charter number in black. TYPE II — Similar, Charter number added in brown.

Back Design: Lincoln Memorial.

SERIES	SIGNATURES	SEAL	A.B.P.	GOOD	V. FINE	UNC.
☐1929 TYPE I	Jones-Woods	Brown	8.50	16.00	32.50	65.00
☐1929 TYPE II	Jones-Woods	Brown	10.00	18.50	40.00	75.00

Face Design: Vignettes of Columbus sighting land. Presentation of an Indian Princess. Red seal. Signatures, Allison-Spinner.

Back Design: California State Seal left, gold coins center, American Eagle right.

DATE	NAME OF BANK	CITY	A.B.P.	GOOD	V. GOOD
☐1870	First National Gold Bank	San Francisco	225.00	450.00	750.00
☐1872	National Gold Bank and Trust Company	San Francisco	275.00	550.00	1000.00
☐1872	National Gold Bank of D.O. Mills and Company	Sacramento	275.00	550.00	1000.00
☐1873	First National Gold Bank	Santa Barbara	275.00	550.00	850.00
☐1873	First National Gold Bank	Stockton	275.00	550.00	850.00
☐1874	Farmers Nat'l Gold Bank	San Jose	275.00	550.00	850.00

FIVE DOLLAR NOTES (1886-1891) SILVER CERTIFICATES
(Large Size)

Face Design: Portrait of President Grant.

Back Design: Five silver dollars.

SERIES	SIGNATURES	SEAL	A.B.P.	GOOD	V. FINE	UNC.
☐1886	Rosecrans-Jordan	Red	65.00	135.00	425.00	4500.00
☐1886	Rosecrans-Hyatt	Red Sm.	65.00	135.00	425.00	4500.00
☐1886	Rosecrans-Hyatt	Red Lg.	65.00	135.00	425.00	4500.00
☐1886	Rosecrans-Huston	Red Lg.	65.00	135.00	425.00	4500.00
☐1886	Rosecrans-Huston	Brown	65.00	135.00	425.00	4500.00
☐1886	Rosecrans-Nebeker	Brown	65.00	135.00	425.00	4500.00
☐1886	Rosecrans-Nebeker	Red Sm.	65.00	135.00	450.00	5000.00

Face Design: Similar to previous Note.

Back Design: Revised.

SERIES	SIGNATURES	SEAL	A.B.P.	GOOD	V. FINE	UNC.
☐1891	Rosecrans-Nebeker	Red	42.50	75.00	400.00	3500.00
☐1891	Tillman-Morgan	Red	42.50	75.00	400.00	3500.00

Face Design: Five Females representing electricity as the dominant force in the world.

LAST NOTE OF THE POPULAR EDUCATIONAL SERIES

Back Design: Portrait of General Grant and General Sheridan.

SERIES	SIGNATURES	SEAL	A.B.P.	GOOD	V. FINE	UNC.
☐ 1896	Tillman-Morgan	Red	55.00	120.00	700.00	6000.00
☐ 1896	Bruce-Roberts	Red	55.00	120.00	700.00	6000.00
☐ 1896	Lyons-Roberts	Red	60.00	175.00	725.00	6500.00

Face Design: Portrait of Indian Chief.

Back Design: Green "V" and "5".

SERIES	SIGNATURES	SEAL	A.B.P.	GOOD	V. FINE	UNC.
☐ 1899	Lyons-Roberts	Blue	37.50	65.00	200.00	1750.00
☐ 1899	Lyons-Treat	Blue	37.50	65.00	200.00	1750.00
☐ 1899	Vernon-Treat	Blue	37.50	65.00	200.00	1750.00
☐ 1899	Vernon-McClung	Blue	37.50	65.00	200.00	1750.00
☐ 1899	Napier-McClung	Blue	37.50	65.00	200.00	1750.00
☐ 1899	Napier-Thompson	Blue	140.00	225.00	650.00	2200.00
☐ 1899	Parker-Burke	Blue	37.50	65.00	200.00	1750.00
☐ 1899	Teehee-Burke	Blue	37.50	65.00	200.00	1750.00
☐ 1899	Elliott-Burke	Blue	37.50	65.00	200.00	1750.00
☐ 1899	Elliott-White	Blue	37.50	65.00	200.00	1750.00
☐ 1899	Speelman-White	Blue	37.50	65.00	200.00	1750.00

FIVE DOLLAR NOTES (1923) SILVER CERTIFICATES
(Large Size)

NOTE NO. 49

Face Design: Portrait of President Lincoln in oval, nicknamed "Porthole Note", blue seal left, blue "5" right.

Back Design: Obverse of Great Seal of the United States.

SERIES	SIGNATURES	SEAL	A.B.P.	GOOD	V. FINE	UNC.
☐1923	Speelman-White	Blue	45.00	75.00	330.00	2000.00

First Issue — small size of $5.00 Silver Certificates 1934.

Face Design: Portrait of President Lincoln, blue "5" to left, blue seal to right.

Back Design: All small size $5.00 notes have the same back design.

SERIES	SIGNATURES	SEAL	A.B.P.	GOOD	V. FINE	UNC.
☐1934	Julian-Morgenthau	Blue	5.50	7.00	10.00	20.00
☐1934A	Julian-Morgenthau	Blue	5.50	7.00	10.00	16.00
☐1934A	Julian-Morgenthau	Yellow	6.50	10.00	18.00	85.00

This note, with Yellow Treasury Seal was a Special Issue during World War II, for military use in combat areas of North Africa and Europe.

SERIES	SIGNATURES	SEAL	A.B.P.	GOOD	V. FINE	UNC.
☐1934B	Julian-Vinson	Blue	6.50	10.00	15.00	35.00
☐1934C	Julian-Snyder	Blue	5.50	7.00	10.00	17.50
☐1934D	Clark-Snyder	Blue	5.50	7.00	10.00	16.00

Face Design: The following Notes are similar to the previous Note. The face design has been revised. Gray "5" replaces blue "5" to left of Lincoln. Blue seal is slightly smaller.

Back Design: Same as previous Note.

SERIES	SIGNATURES	SEAL	A.B.P.	GOOD	V. FINE	UNC.
☐ 1953	Priest-Humphrey	Blue	——	——	5.50	15.00
☐ 1953A	Priest-Anderson	Blue	——	——	5.50	13.25
☐ 1953B	Smith-Dillon	Blue	——	——	5.50	13.25

Production of Five Dollar Silver Certificates ended in 1962.

Face Design: Portrait of General George Henry Thomas (1816-1870) the
"Rock of Chickamaugua".

Back Design: NOTE NO. 52

SERIES	SIGNATURES	SEAL	A.B.P.	GOOD	V. FINE	UNC.
☐1890	Rosecrans-Huston	Brown	75.00	140.00	575.00	2200.00
☐1890	Rosecrans-Nebeker	Brown	75.00	140.00	575.00	2200.00
☐1890	Rosecrans-Nebeker	Red	75.00	140.00	575.00	2600.00

Face Design: Same as previous Note
Back Design: NOTE NO. 53.

SERIES	SIGNATURES	SEAL	A.B.P.	GOOD	V. FINE	UNC.
☐1891	Rosecrans-Nebeker	Red	50.00	95.00	265.00	1250.00
☐1891	Tillman-Morgan	Red	50.00	95.00	265.00	1250.00
☐1891	Bruce-Roberts	Red	50.00	95.00	265.00	1250.00
☐1891	Lyons-Roberts	Red	52.50	100.00	330.00	2250.00

Face Design: Portrait of President Lincoln center, Federal Reserve Seal left, Treasury Seal right.

Back Design: Scene of Columbus in sight of land left, Landing of Pilgrims right.

Series of 1914—red Treasury Seal and red numbers.

SERIES	CITY	SIGNATURES	SEAL	A.B.P.	GOOD	V. FINE	UNC.
☐1914	Boston	Burke-McAdoo	Red	15.00	30.00	72.50	500.00
☐1914	New York	Burke-McAdoo	Red	15.00	30.00	70.00	450.00
☐1914	Philadelphia	Burke-McAdoo	Red	15.00	30.00	70.00	450.00
☐1914	Cleveland	Burke-McAdoo	Red	15.00	30.00	70.00	450.00
☐1914	Richmond	Burke-McAdoo	Red	15.00	30.00	70.00	450.00
☐1914	Atlanta	Burke-McAdoo	Red	15.00	30.00	70.00	450.00
☐1914	Chicago	Burke-McAdoo	Red	15.00	30.00	70.00	450.00
☐1914	St. Louis	Burke-McAdoo	Red	15.00	30.00	70.00	450.00
☐1914	Minneapolis	Burke-McAdoo	Red	15.00	30.00	70.00	450.00
☐1914	Kansas City	Burke-McAdoo	Red	15.00	30.00	70.00	450.00
☐1914	Dallas	Burke-McAdoo	Red	15.00	30.00	70.00	450.00
☐1914	San Francisco	Burke-McAdoo	Red	15.00	30.00	75.00	525.00

FIVE DOLLAR NOTES (1914) FEDERAL RESERVE NOTES

Series of 1914—blue Treasury Seal and blue numbers. **NOTE NO. 54A**

SERIES	CITY	SIGNATURES	SEAL	A.B.P.	GOOD	V. FINE	UNC.
☐ 1914	Boston	Burke-McAdoo	Blue	6.00	10.00	16.00	180.00
☐ 1914	Boston	Burke-Glass	Blue	7.50	12.00	20.00	180.00
☐ 1914	Boston	Burke-Huston	Blue	6.00	10.00	16.50	180.00
☐ 1914	Boston	White-Mellon	Blue	6.00	10.00	16.50	180.00
☐ 1914	New York	Burke-McAdoo	Blue	6.00	10.00	16.50	180.00
☐ 1914	New York	Burke-Glass	Blue	6.50	12.50	20.00	180.00
☐ 1914	New York	Burke-Huston	Blue	6.00	10.00	16.50	180.00
☐ 1914	New York	White-Mellon	Blue	6.00	10.00	16.50	180.00
☐ 1914	Philadelphia	Burke-McAdoo	Blue	6.00	10.00	16.50	180.00
☐ 1914	Philadelphia	Burke-Glass	Blue	6.50	12.50	22.00	200.00
☐ 1914	Philadelphia	Burke-Huston	Blue	6.00	10.00	16.50	180.00
☐ 1914	Philadelphia	White-Mellon	Blue	6.00	10.00	16.50	180.00
☐ 1914	Cleveland	Burke-McAdoo	Blue	6.00	10.00	16.50	180.00
☐ 1914	Cleveland	Burke-Glass	Blue	6.50	12.50	20.00	180.00
☐ 1914	Cleveland	Burke-Huston	Blue	6.00	10.00	16.50	180.00
☐ 1914	Cleveland	White-Mellon	Blue	6.00	10.00	16.50	180.00
☐ 1914	Richmond	Burke-McAdoo	Blue	6.50	12.50	20.00	180.00
☐ 1914	Richmond	Burke-Glass	Blue	6.50	12.50	20.00	225.00
☐ 1914	Richmond	Burke-Huston	Blue	6.50	12.00	17.50	180.00
☐ 1914	Richmond	White-Mellon	Blue	6.50	12.00	17.50	180.00
☐ 1914	Atlanta	Burke-McAdoo	Blue	6.00	10.00	16.50	180.00
☐ 1914	Atlanta	Burke-Glass	Blue	7.50	15.00	25.00	225.00
☐ 1914	Atlanta	Burke-Huston	Blue	6.00	10.00	16.50	180.00
☐ 1914	Atlanta	White-Mellon	Blue	6.00	10.00	16.50	180.00
☐ 1914	Chicago	Burke-McAdoo	Blue	6.00	10.00	16.50	180.00
☐ 1914	Chicago	Burke-Glass	Blue	6.50	12.50	20.00	180.00
☐ 1914	Chicago	Burke-Huston	Blue	6.00	10.00	16.50	180.00
☐ 1914	Chicago	White-Mellon	Blue	6.00	10.00	16.50	180.00
☐ 1914	St. Louis	Burke-McAdoo	Blue	6.00	10.00	16.50	180.00
☐ 1914	St. Louis	Burke-Glass	Blue	6.50	12.50	22.00	180.00
☐ 1914	St. Louis	Burke-Huston	Blue	6.00	10.00	16.50	180.00
☐ 1914	St. Louis	White-Mellon	Blue	6.00	10.00	16.50	180.00
☐ 1914	Minneapolis	Burke-McAdoo	Blue	6.00	10.00	16.50	180.00
☐ 1914	Minneapolis	Burke-Glass	Blue	7.50	15.00	28.00	225.00
☐ 1914	Minneapolis	Burke-Huston	Blue	6.00	10.00	16.50	180.00
☐ 1914	Minneapolis	White-Mellon	Blue	6.00	10.00	16.50	180.00
☐ 1914	Kansas City	Burke-McAdoo	Blue	6.00	10.00	16.50	180.00
☐ 1914	Kansas City	Burke-Glass	Blue	6.50	12.50	20.00	180.00
☐ 1914	Kansas City	Burke-Huston	Blue	6.00	10.00	16.50	180.00
☐ 1914	Kansas City	White-Mellon	Blue	6.00	10.00	16.50	180.00
☐ 1914	Dallas	Burke-McAdoo	Blue	7.50	15.00	25.00	225.00
☐ 1914	Dallas	Burke-Glass	Blue	7.50	15.00	22.00	225.00
☐ 1914	Dallas	Burke-Huston	Blue	6.00	10.00	16.50	180.00
☐ 1914	Dallas	White-Mellon	Blue	6.00	10.00	16.50	180.00
☐ 1914	San Francisco	Burke-McAdoo	Blue	6.50	12.50	20.00	180.00
☐ 1914	San Francisco	Burke-Glass	Blue	6.50	12.50	20.00	180.00
☐ 1914	San Francisco	Burke-Huston	Blue	-6.50	12.50	20.00	180.00
☐ 1914	San Francisco	White-Mellon	Blue	6.50	12.50	20.00	180.00

FIVE DOLLAR NOTES (1928) FEDERAL RESERVE NOTES
(Small Size)   NOTE NO. 55

Face Design: Portrait of President Lincoln center, black Federal Reserve Seal with numeral for district in center. City of issuing bank in seal circle. Green Treasury Seal to right.

Back Design: Similar to Note No. 50,
Lincoln Memorial in Washington, D.C.

SERIES OF 1928 — SIGNATURES OF TATE AND MELLON, GREEN SEAL

BANK	A.B.P.	GOOD	V.FINE	UNC.	BANK	A.B.P.	GOOD	V.FINE	UNC.
☐Boston	6.00	8.00	12.00	30.00	☐Chicago . . .	6.00	8.00	12.00	24.00
☐New York . .	6.00	8.00	12.00	24.00	☐St. Louis . . .	6.00	8.00	12.00	30.00
☐Philadelphia	6.00	8.00	12.00	26.00	☐Minneapolis	6.00	8.00	12.00	32.00
☐Cleveland . .	6.50	8.00	12.00	27.50	☐Kansas City .	6.00	8.00	12.00	30.00
☐Richmond . .	6.00	8.00	12.00	32.00	☐Dallas	6.00	8.00	12.00	30.00
☐Atlanta	6.00	8.00	12.00	30.00	☐San Francisco	6.00	8.00	12.00	26.00

SERIES OF 1928A — SIGNATURES OF WOODS-MELLON, GREEN SEAL

BANK	A.B.P.	GOOD	V.FINE	UNC.	BANK	A.B.P.	GOOD	V.FINE	UNC.
☐Boston	6.00	8.00	12.00	37.50	☐Chicago . . .	6.00	8.00	12.00	30.00
☐New York . .	6.00	8.00	12.00	32.50	☐St. Louis . . .	6.00	8.00	12.00	37.50
☐Philadelphia	6.00	8.00	12.00	35.00	☐Minneapolis	6.00	8.00	12.00	42.00
☐Cleveland . .	6.00	8.00	12.00	35.00	☐Kansas City .	6.00	8.00	12.00	42.00
☐Richmond . .	6.00	8.00	12.00	42.00	☐Dallas	6.00	8.00	12.00	42.00
☐Atlanta	6.00	8.00	12.00	37.50	☐San Francisco	6.00	8.00	12.00	36.00

SERIES OF 1928B—SIGNATURES OF WOODS-MELLON, GREEN SEAL
BLACK FEDERAL RESERVE SEAL NOW HAS A LETTER FOR
DISTRICT IN PLACE OF THE NUMERAL
(Small Size)

D

                                                              NOTE NO. 55A

BANK	A.B.P.	GOOD	V.FINE	UNC.	BANK	A.B.P.	GOOD	V.FINE	UNC.
☐Boston	6.00	8.00	12.00	35.00	☐Chicago . . .	6.00	8.00	12.00	35.00
☐New York . .	6.00	8.00	12.00	35.00	☐St. Louis . . .	6.00	8.00	12.00	35.00
☐Philadelphia	6.00	8.00	12.00	35.00	☐Minneapolis	6.00	8.00	12.00	40.00
☐Cleveland . .	6.00	8.00	12.00	35.00	☐Kansas City .	6.00	8.00	12.00	40.00
☐Richmond . .	6.00	8.00	12.00	37.50	☐Dallas	6.00	8.00	12.00	37.50
☐Atlanta	6.00	8.00	12.00	35.00	☐San Francisco	6.00	8.00	12.00	30.00

FIVE DOLLAR NOTES (1928) FEDERAL RESERVE NOTES

SERIES OF 1928C — SIGNATURES OF WOODS-MILLS, GREEN SEAL

BANK	A.B.P.	GOOD	V.FINE	UNC.	BANK	A.B.P.	GOOD	V.FINE	UNC.
☐ Cleveland	20.00	42.50	85.00	275.00	☐ San				
☐ Atlanta	20.00	42.50	85.00	275.00	Francisco	22.50	45.00	95.00	325.00

This series not issued by other banks.

SERIES OF 1928D — SIGNATURES OF WOODS-WOODIN, GREEN SEAL

BANK	A.B.P.	GOOD	V.FINE	UNC.
☐ Atlanta	50.00	80.00	200.00	650.00

This series not issued by other banks.

SERIES OF 1934 — JULIAN-MORGENTHAU, GREEN SEAL

("Redeemable in Gold" removed from obligation over Federal Reserve Seal.)

Note: The Green Treasury Seal on this note is known in a light and dark color. The light seal is worth about 10% to 20% more in most cases.

BANK	A.B.P.	V.FINE	UNC.	BANK	A.B.P.	V.FINE	UNC.
☐ Boston	6.00	12.00	30.00	☐ Kansas City	6.00	12.00	30.00
☐ New York	6.00	12.00	30.00	☐ Dallas	6.00	12.00	30.00
☐ Philadelphia	6.00	12.00	30.00	☐ San Francisco	6.00	12.00	30.00
☐ Cleveland	6.00	12.00	30.00	☐ San Francisco*	9.50	35.00	200.00
☐ Richmond	6.00	12.00	30.00				
☐ Atlanta	6.00	12.00	30.00	*This note with BROWN Treasury			
☐ Chicago	6.00	12.00	30.00	Seal and surcharged HAWAII. For			
☐ St. Louis	6.00	12.00	30.00	use in Pacific area of Operations			
☐ Minneapolis	6.00	12.00	30.00	during World War II.			

(Small Size)

NOTE NO. 56

SERIES OF 1934-1934A— 1934A-JULIAN-MORGENTHAU, Surprinted HAWAII, used in Pacific area during World War II. Used with Brown Treasury Seal.

SERIES OF 1934A — JULIAN-MORGENTHAU, GREEN SEAL

BANK	A.B.P.	V.FINE	UNC.	BANK	A.B.P.	V.FINE	UNC.
☐ Boston	5.50	10.00	27.50	☐ San Francisco	6.00	12.00	28.00
☐ New York	5.50	10.00	25.00	☐ San Francisco*	12.00	25.00	100.00
☐ Philadelphia	5.50	10.00	27.50				
☐ Cleveland	5.50	10.00	27.50				
☐ Richmond	6.00	12.50	28.00	*This note with BROWN			
☐ Atlanta	5.50	12.00	25.00	Treasury Seal and surcharged			
☐ Chicago	5.50	12.00	25.00	HAWAII. For use in Pacific area			
☐ St. Louis	5.50	12.00	28.00	of operations during World War II.			

FIVE DOLLAR NOTES (1934) FEDERAL RESERVE NOTES
(Small Size)

Face Design: Same as Note No. 55. **Back Design:** Same as Note No. 50

SERIES OF 1934B — SIGNATURES OF JULIAN-VINSON, GREEN SEAL

BANK & CITY	A.B.P.	V.FINE	UNC.	BANK & CITY	A.B.P.	V.FINE	UNC.
☐Boston	6.00	15.00	35.00	☐Chicago	6.00	12.50	35.00
☐New York	6.00	12.50	35.00	☐St. Louis	6.00	20.00	35.00
☐Philadelphia	6.00	12.50	35.00	☐Minneapolis	6.00	20.00	35.00
☐Cleveland	6.00	12.50	35.00	☐Kansas City	8.00	20.00	50.00
☐Richmond	6.00	15.00	35.00	☐Dallas		Not Issued	
☐Atlanta	6.00	15.00	35.00	☐San Francisco	8.00	15.00	35.00

SERIES OF 1934C — SIGNATURES OF JULIAN-SNYDER, GREEN SEAL

BANK & CITY	A.B.P.	V.FINE	UNC.	BANK & CITY	A.B.P.	V.FINE	UNC.
☐Boston	5.50	10.00	25.00	☐Chicago	5.50	10.00	25.00
☐New York	5.50	10.00	25.00	☐St. Louis	5.50	10.00	25.00
☐Philadelphia	5.50	10.00	25.00	☐Minneapolis	5.50	10.00	27.50
☐Cleveland	5.50	10.00	25.00	☐Kansas City	5.50	10.00	25.00
☐Richmond	5.50	10.00	25.00	☐Dallas	5.50	10.00	27.50
☐Atlanta	5.50	10.00	25.00	☐San Francisco	5.50	10.00	25.00

SERIES OF 1934D — SIGNATURES OF CLARK-SNYDER, GREEN SEAL

BANK & CITY	A.B.P.	V.FINE	UNC.	BANK & CITY	A.B.P.	V.FINE	UNC.
☐Boston	5.50	8.50	18.50	☐Chicago	5.50	8.50	17.50
☐New York	5.50	8.50	15.00	☐St. Louis	5.50	10.00	20.00
☐Philadelphia	5.50	8.50	18.50	☐Minneapolis	5.50	10.00	20.00
☐Cleveland	5.50	8.50	20.00	☐Kansas City	5.50	10.00	20.00
☐Richmond	5.50	8.50	18.50	☐Dallas	6.00	12.00	22.00
☐Atlanta	5.50	10.00	18.50	☐San Francisco	5.50	8.50	18.50

FIVE DOLLAR NOTES (1950) FEDERAL RESERVE NOTES
BLACK FEDERAL RESERVE SEAL AND GREEN TREASURY SEALS
ARE NOW SMALLER

(Small Size)

Face Design: Similar to Note No. 55. **Back Design:** Similar to Note No. 50.

SERIES OF 1950 — SIGNATURES OF CLARK-SNYDER, GREEN SEAL

BANK & CITY	A.B.P.	V.FINE	UNC.	BANK & CITY	A.B.P.	V.FINE	UNC.
☐ Boston	5.50	8.00	15.00	☐ Chicago	5.50	8.00	15.00
☐ New York	5.50	8.00	13.00	☐ St. Louis	5.50	8.00	16.00
☐ Philadelphia	5.50	8.00	14.50	☐ Minneapolis	5.50	8.00	18.50
☐ Cleveland	5.50	8.00	14.50	☐ Kansas City	5.50	8.00	16.00
☐ Richmond	5.50	8.00	14.00	☐ Dallas	5.50	8.00	16.00
☐ Atlanta	5.50	8.00	14.50	☐ San Francisco	5.50	8.00	15.00

SERIES OF 1950A — PRIEST-HUMPHREY, GREEN SEAL

Boston 14.00	Cleveland 14.00	Chicago 14.00	Kansas City 14.00
New York 14.00	Richmond 14.00	St. Louis 15.00	Dallas 14.00
Philadelphia 14.00	Atlanta 14.00	Minneapolis 15.00	San Francisco 14.00

SERIES OF 1950B — PRIEST-ANDERSON, GREEN SEAL

Boston 13.00	Cleveland 12.50	Chicago 11.50	Kansas City 14.00
New York 12.50	Richmond 12.50	St. Louis 15.00	Dallas 13.00
Philadelphia 12.50	Atlanta 12.50	Minneapolis 17.50	San Francisco 14.00

SERIES OF 1950C — SMITH-DILLON, GREEN SEAL

Boston 12.50	Cleveland 12.50	Chicago 14.00	Kansas City 14.00
New York 11.00	Richmond 12.50	St. Louis 12.50	Dallas 17.50
Philadelphia 12.50	Atlanta 12.50	Minneapolis 14.00	San Francisco 15.00

SERIES OF 1950D — GRANAHAN-DILLON, GREEN SEAL

Boston 12.00	Cleveland 12.00	Chicago 11.00	Kansas City 12.50
New York 12.00	Richmond 11.00	St. Louis 11.50	Dallas 12.50
Philadelphia 12.00	Atlanta 12.00	Minneapolis 12.50	San Francisco 12.00

SERIES OF 1950E — GRANAHAN-FOWLER, GREEN SEAL

New York 13.00   Chicago 15.00   San Francisco 14.00
This Note was issued by only three banks.

FIVE DOLLAR NOTES (1963) FEDERAL RESERVE NOTES
("IN GOD WE TRUST" IS ADDED ON THE BACK)
(Small Size)   NOTE NO. 57A

SERIES OF 1963 — GRANAHAN-DILLON, GREEN SEAL

Boston......14.00	Cleveland ...13.00	Chicago.....13.00	Kansas City ..16.00
New York ...13.00	Richmond ...NONE	St. Louis 13.00	Dallas 15.00
Philadelphia..12.00	Atlanta......13.00	Minneapolis ..NONE	San Francisco 14.00

SERIES OF 1963A — GRANAHAN-FOWLER, GREEN SEAL

Boston......11.00	Cleveland ...11.00	Chicago.....11.00	Kansas City ..12.00
New York ...13.00	Richmond ...NONE	St. Louis 11.00	Dallas 11.50
Philadelphia..11.00	Atlanta......11.00	Minneapolis..11.00	San Francisco 11.50

FIVE DOLLAR NOTES (1969) FEDERAL RESERVE NOTES
(WORDING IN GREEN TREASURY SEAL CHANGED FROM LATIN TO ENGLISH)
(Small Size)   NOTE NO. 57B

SERIES OF 1969 — ELSTON-KENNEDY, GREEN SEAL

Boston.......9.50	Cleveland 9.50	Chicago.....10.00	Kansas City ..11.00
New York ...9.50	Richmond 9.50	St. Louis 9.50	Dallas ..10.50
Philadelphia..9.50	Atlanta.....9.50	Minneapolis ..10.00	San Francisco 10.00

SERIES OF 1969A — KABIS-CONNALLY, GREEN SEAL

Boston.......8.50	Cleveland 8.50	Chicago......8.50	Kansas City ..8.50
New York ...8.50	Richmond 8.50	St. Louis 8.50	Dallas 8.50
Philadelphia..8.50	Atlanta......8.50	Minneapolis ..8.50	San Francisco .8.50

$5.00

FIVE DOLLAR NOTES (1969) FEDERAL RESERVE NOTES
(WORDING IN GREEN TREASURY SEAL CHANGED FROM LATIN TO ENGLISH)
(Small Size)   NOTE NO. 57B

SERIES OF 1969B — BANUELOS-CONNALLY, GREEN SEAL

Boston 8.50	Cleveland 8.50	Chicago 8.50	Kansas City . . . 8.50
New York 8.50	Richmond . . . 8.50	St. Louis 8.50	Dallas 8.50
Philadelphia . . . 8.50	Atlanta 8.50	Minneapolis . . . 8.50	San Francisco . 8.50

SERIES OF 1969C — BANUELOS-SHULTZ, GREEN SEAL

Boston 8.00	Cleveland 8.00	Chicago 8.00	Kansas City . . . 8.00
New York 8.00	Richmond . . . 8.00	St. Louis 8.00	Dallas 8.00
Philadelphia . . . 8.00	Atlanta 8.00	Minneapolis . . . 8.00	San Francisco . 8.00

SERIES OF 1974 — NEFF-SIMON, GREEN SEAL

Boston 7.50	Cleveland 7.50	Chicago 7.50	Kansas City . . . 7.50
New York 7.50	Richmond . . . 7.50	St. Louis 7.50	Dallas 7.50
Philadelphia . . . 7.50	Atlanta 7.50	Minneapolis . . . 7.50	San Francisco . 7.50

SERIES OF 1977 — MORTON-BLUMENTHAL, GREEN SEAL

Boston 7.50	Cleveland 7.50	Chicago 7.50	Kansas City . . . 7.50
New York 7.50	Richmond . . . 7.50	St. Louis 7.50	Dallas 7.50
Philadelphia . . . 7.50	Atlanta 7.50	Minneapolis . . . 7.50	San Francisco . 7.50

SERIES OF 1977A — MORTON-MILLER, GREEN SEAL
This series is now in production. All notes are current.

FIVE DOLLAR NOTES (1918) FEDERAL RESERVE BANK NOTES
(ALL WITH BLUE SEAL AND BLUE SERIAL NUMBERS)
(Large Size)   NOTE NO. 58

Face Design: Portrait of President Lincoln with Reserve City in center.
Back Design: Same as Note No. 54.

BANK & CITY	SERIES	GOVERNMENT SIGNATURES	BANK SIGNATURES	A.B.P.	GOOD	V. FINE	UNC.
☐Boston	1918	Teehee-Burke	Bullen-Morse	80.00	150.00	750.00	4000.00
☐New York	1918	Teehee-Burke	Hendricks-Strong	15.00	25.00	55.00	675.00
☐Phila.	1918	Teehee-Burke	Hardt-Passmore	15.00	25.00	55.00	675.00
☐Phila.	1918	Teehee-Burke	Dyer-Passmore	15.00	25.00	55.00	675.00
☐Cleveland	1918	Teehee-Burke	Baxter-Fancher	15.00	25.00	55.00	600.00
☐Cleveland	1918	Teehee-Burke	Davis-Fancher	15.00	25.00	60.00	625.00
☐Cleveland	1918	Elliott-Burke	Davis-Fancher	15.00	35.00	55.00	600.00
☐Atlanta	1915	Teehee-Burke	Bell-Wellborn	40.00	75.00	210.00	1000.00
☐Atlanta	1915	Teehee-Burke	Pike-McCord	25.00	40.00	100.00	700.00
☐Atlanta	1918	Teehee-Burke	Pike-McCord	15.00	25.00	55.00	675.00
☐Atlanta	1918	Teehee-Burke	Bell-Wellborn	15.00	25.00	55.00	675.00
☐Atlanta	1918	Elliott-Burke	Bell-Wellborn	15.00	25.00	55.00	675.00
☐Chicago	1915	Teehee-Burke	McLallen-McDougal	15.00	25.00	55.00	600.00
☐Chicago	1918	Teehee-Burke	McCloud-McDougal	12.00	25.00	55.00	175.00
☐Chicago	1918	Teehee-Burke	Cramer-McDougal	15.00	25.00	60.00	675.00
☐St. Louis	1918	Teehee-Burke	Attebery-Wells	15.00	25.00	60.00	675.00
☐St. Louis	1918	Teehee-Burke	Attebery-Biggs	15.00	25.00	75.00	675.00
☐St. Louis	1918	Elliott-Burke	White-Biggs	15.00	25.00	60.00	675.00
☐Minn.	1918	Teehee-Burke	Cook-Wold	30.00	50.00	60.00	700.00
☐Kan. City	1915	Teehee-Burke	Anderson-Miller	15.00	25.00	125.00	600.00
☐Kan. City	1915	Teehee-Burke	Cross-Miller	15.00	25.00	60.00	500.00
☐Kan. City	1915	Teehee-Burke	Helm-Miller	30.00	50.00	60.00	500.00
☐Kan. City	1918	Teehee-Burke	Anderson-Miller	20.00	30.00	125.00	600.00
☐Kan. City	1918	Elliott-Burke	Helm-Miller	20.00	30.00	80.00	675.00
☐Dallas	1915	Teehee-Burke	Hoopes-VanZandt	30.00	50.00	125.00	600.00
☐Dallas	1915	Teehee-Burke	Talley-VanZandt	35.00	60.00	150.00	600.00
☐Dallas	1915	Teehee-Burke	Talley-VanZandt	20.00	30.00	100.00	600.00
☐San Fran.	1915	Teehee-Burke	Clerk-Lynch	25.00	40.00	200.00	600.00
☐San Fran.	1918	Teehee-Burke	Clerk-Lynch	25.00	40.00	200.00	675.00

$5.00

FIVE DOLLAR NOTES (1929) FEDERAL RESERVE BANK NOTES
(Small Size)

Face Design: Portrait of President Lincoln.

SERIES 1929—brown seal.

BANK & CITY	SIGNATURES	A.B.P.	GOOD	V. FINE	UNC.
☐Boston	Jones-Woods	6.00	10.00	20.00	60.00
☐New York	Jones-Woods	6.00	12.50	25.00	60.00
☐Philadelphia	Jones-Woods	6.00	10.00	20.00	60.00
☐Cleveland	Jones-Woods	6.00	10.00	20.00	60.00
☐Atlanta	Jones-Woods	6.00	12.50	35.00	80.00
☐Chicago	Jones-Woods	6.00	8.00	20.00	60.00
☐St. Louis	Jones-Woods	8.00	20.00	125.00	350.00
☐Minneapolis	Jones-Woods	7.00	17.50	35.00	80.00
☐Kansas City	Jones-Woods	6.00	10.00	20.00	72.50
☐Dallas	Jones-Woods	6.00	12.50	25.00	75.00
☐San Francisco	Jones-Woods	12.00	17.50	500.00	2000.00

TEN DOLLAR NOTES

ORDER OF ISSUE

$10.00

TEN DOLLAR NOTES (1861) DEMAND NOTES
NO TREASURY SEAL

(Large Size)

Face Design: Portrait of President Lincoln left, female figure with sword and shield.

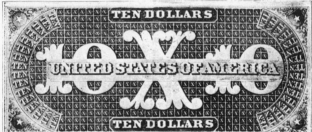

Back Design: Ornate designs of "TEN".

CITY	A.B.P.	GOOD	V.GOOD
☐ Boston (I)	250.00	800.00	2000.00
☐ New York (I)	225.00	700.00	2000.00
☐ Philadelphia (I)	225.00	700.00	2000.00
☐ Cincinnati (I)	400.00	1200.00	RARE
☐ St. Louis (I)	300.00	900.00	RARE
☐ Boston (II)	500.00	1150.00	1500.00
☐ New York (II)	500.00	1150.00	1500.00
☐ Philadelphia (II)	500.00	1150.00	1500.00
☐ Cincinnati (II)	500.00	1150.00	1500.00
☐ St. Louis (II)	500.00	1150.00	1500.00

TEN DOLLAR NOTES (1862-1863) UNITED STATES NOTES
(ALSO KNOWN AS LEGAL TENDER NOTES)
(Large Size)

Back Design
Face Design: Similar to previous Note.

SERIES	SIGNATURES	SEAL	A.B.P.	GOOD	V. FINE	UNC.
☐ 1862	Chittenden-Spinner*	Red	45.00	100.00	300.00	2250.00
☐ 1862	Chittenden-Spinner**	Red	75.00	150.00	350.00	2500.00
☐ 1863	Chittenden-Spinner**	Red	70.00	150.00	400.00	2400.00

*First Obligation: Similar to Note No. 33   **Second Obligation: Shown above.

TEN DOLLAR NOTES (1869) UNITED STATES NOTES
(Large Size)

Face Design: Portrait of Daniel Webster left, presentation of Indian Princess right. (This note is nicknamed "Jackass Note", because the EAGLE between the signatures resembles a donkey when it is held upside down.)

SERIES	SIGNATURES	SEAL	A.B.P.	GOOD	V. FINE	UNC.
☐ 1869	Allison-Spinner	Red	60.00	125.00	400.00	2200.00

Face Design: Similar to previous Note.

Back Design: Revised

SERIES	SIGNATURES	SEAL	A.B.P.	GOOD	V. FINE	UNC.
☐ 1875	Allison-New	Red	30.00	50.00	175.00	1400.00
☐ Same as above — SERIES A		Red	30.00	45.00	145.00	1250.00
☐ 1878	Allison-Gilfillan	Red	27.50	45.00	140.00	1200.00
☐ 1880	Scofield-Gilfillan	Brown	20.00	45.00	100.00	1400.00
☐ 1880	Bruce-Gilfillan	Brown	22.50	45.00	100.00	1400.00
☐ 1880	Bruce-Wyman	Brown	22.50	45.00	100.00	1400.00
☐ 1880	Bruce-Wyman	Red Plain	22.50	45.00	150.00	1500.00
☐ 1880	Rosecrans-Jordan	Red Plain	22.50	45.00	150.00	1500.00
☐ 1880	Rosecrans-Hyatt	Red Plain	22.50	45.00	150.00	1500.00
☐ 1880	Rosecrans-Hyatt	Red Spikes	22.50	45.00	200.00	1400.00
☐ 1880	Rosecrans-Huston	Red Spikes	22.50	45.00	175.00	1400.00
☐ 1880	Rosecrans-Huston	Brown	22.50	45.00	175.00	1550.00
☐ 1880	Rosecrans-Nebeker	Brown	22.50	45.00	175.00	1550.00
☐ 1880	Rosecrans-Nebeker	Red	22.50	45.00	100.00	1250.00
☐ 1880	Tillman-Morgan	Red	22.50	45.00	100.00	1250.00
☐ 1880	Bruce-Roberts	Red	22.50	45.00	100.00	1250.00
☐ 1880	Lyons-Roberts	Red	22.50	45.00	100.00	1250.00

TEN DOLLAR NOTES (1901) UNITED STATES NOTES

LEGAL TENDER (Large Size)   **NOTE NO. 64**

Face Design: American Bison (buffalo) center, portrait of Lewis left, portrait of Clark right.

$10.00

Back Design: Female allegorical figure in arch.

SERIES	SIGNATURES	SEAL	A.B.P.	GOOD	V. FINE	UNC.
☐1901	Lyons-Roberts	Red	35.00	70.00	350.00	2000.00
☐1901	Lyons-Treat	Red	35.00	70.00	350.00	2000.00
☐1901	Vernon-Treat	Red	35.00	70.00	350.00	2000.00
☐1901	Vernon-McClung	Red	35.00	70.00	350.00	2000.00
☐1901	Napier-McClung	Red	35.00	70.00	350.00	2000.00
☐1901	Parker-Burke	Red	35.00	70.00	350.00	2000.00
☐1901	Teehee-Burke	Red	35.00	70.00	350.00	2000.00
☐1901	Elliott-White	Red	35.00	70.00	350.00	2000.00
☐1901	Speelman-White	Red	35.00	70.00	350.00	2000.00

Face Design: Portrait of President Jackson center, red seal left, red "X" to right.

Back Design

SERIES	SIGNATURES	SEAL	A.B.P.	GOOD	V. FINE	UNC.
☐1923	Speelman-White	Red	125.00	225.00	500.00	4750.00

Face Design: Benjamin Franklin and kite left, name of bank and city center. Effigy of Liberty and Eagle right.

Back Design: Border green, center black. DeSoto on horseback at Mississippi River.

	SERIES	SIGNATURES	SEAL	A.B.P.	GOOD	V. FINE	UNC.
☐	Original	Chittenden-Spinner	Red	75.00	150.00	220.00	2250.00
☐	Original	Colby-Spinner	Red	75.00	150.00	220.00	2250.00
☐	Original	Jeffries-Spinner	Red	125.00	300.00	800.00	RARE
☐	Original	Allison-Spinner	Red	75.00	150.00	220.00	2100.00
☐	1875	Allison-New	Red	75.00	150.00	260.00	2250.00
☐	1875	Allison-Wyman	Red	75.00	150.00	260.00	2250.00
☐	1875	Allison-Gilfillan	Red	75.00	150.00	260.00	2250.00
☐	1875	Scofield-Gilfillan	Red	75.00	150.00	260.00	2250.00
☐	1875	Bruce-Gilfillan	Red	75.00	150.00	260.00	2250.00
☐	1875	Bruce-Wyman	Red	75.00	150.00	265.00	2350.00
☐	1875	Rosecrans-Huston	Red	75.00	150.00	260.00	2250.00
☐	1875	Rosecrans-Nebeker	Red	75.00	150.00	260.00	2250.00

TEN DOLLAR NOTES (1882) NATIONAL BANK NOTES
SECOND CHARTER PERIOD (Large Size)

First Issue — brown seal and brown backs.

Face Design: Similar to previous Notes No. 66-67.
Back Design: Similar to Note No. 39, but border in brown with green Charter Number

SERIES	SIGNATURES	SEAL	A.B.P.	GOOD	V. FINE	UNC.
☐ 1882	Bruce-Gilfillan	Brown	32.00	55.00	110.00	700.00
☐ 1882	Bruce-Wyman	Brown	32.00	55.00	110.00	700.00
☐ 1882	Bruce-Jordan	Brown	34.00	60.00	220.00	800.00
☐ 1882	Rosecrans-Jordan	Brown	32.00	55.00	110.00	700.00
☐ 1882	Rosecrans-Hyatt	Brown	32.00	55.00	110.00	700.00
☐ 1882	Rosecrans-Huston	Brown	32.00	55.00	110.00	700.00
☐ 1882	Rosecrans-Nebeker	Brown	32.00	55.00	110.00	700.00
☐ 1882	Rosecrans-Morgan	Brown	80.00	175.00	700.00	2750.00
☐ 1882	Tillman-Morgan	Brown	32.00	55.00	110.00	700.00
☐ 1882	Tillman-Roberts	Brown	32.00	55.00	110.00	700.00
☐ 1882	Bruce-Roberts	Brown	32.00	55.00	110.00	700.00
☐ 1882	Lyons-Roberts	Brown	32.00	55.00	110.00	700.00
☐ 1882	Lyons-Treat	Brown	34.00	60.00	220.00	900.00
☐ 1882	Vernon-Treat	Brown	34.00	60.00	220.00	900.00

Second Issue — blue seal, Greenback with date 1882-1908

Face Design: Similar to Note No. 66. **Back Design:** Similar to Note No. 40
(Large Size)

SERIES	SIGNATURES	SEAL	A.B.P.	GOOD	V. FINE	UNC.
☐ 1882	Rosecrans-Huston	Blue	50.00	75.00	220.00	1000.00
☐ 1882	Rosecrans-Nebeker	Blue	50.00	75.00	220.00	1000.00
☐ 1882	Rosecrans-Morgan	Blue	150.00	300.00	700.00	3800.00
☐ 1882	Tillman-Morgan	Blue	50.00	75.00	220.00	1000.00
☐ 1882	Tillman-Roberts	Blue	50.00	75.00	220.00	1200.00
☐ 1882	Bruce-Roberts	Blue	50.00	75.00	220.00	1200.00
☐ 1882	Lyons-Roberts	Blue	50.00	75.00	220.00	1000.00
☐ 1882	Vernon-Treat	Blue	50.00	75.00	220.00	1200.00
☐ 1882	Vernon-McClung	Blue	50.00	75.00	275.00	1350.00
☐ 1882	Napier-McClung	Blue	50.00	75.00	275.00	1350.00

TEN DOLLAR NOTES (1882) NATIONAL BANK NOTES

Third Issue—blue seal, Greenback with value in block letters.

Face Design: Similar to previous Notes (See Note No. 66)
Back Design: Similar to Note No. 41.

SERIES	SIGNATURES	SEAL	A.B.P.	GOOD	V. FINE	UNC.
☐ 1882	Tillman-Roberts	Blue	50.00	95.00	550.00	2000.00
☐ 1882	Lyons-Roberts	Blue	35.00	80.00	550.00	2000.00
☐ 1882	Vernon-Treat	Blue	50.00	95.00	550.00	2000.00
☐ 1882	Napier-McClung	Blue	50.00	95.00	550.00	2000.00

NOTE: These Notes may exist with other signatures, but are very rare.

TEN DOLLAR NOTES (1902) NATIONAL BANK NOTES
THIRD CHARTER PERIOD (Large Size)
NOTE NO. 71

First Issue—red seal and red Charter numbers.

Face Design: Portrait of President McKinley left, name of bank and City in center.

SERIES	SIGNATURES	SEAL	A.B.P.	GOOD	V. FINE	UNC.
☐ 1902	Lyons-Roberts	Red	50.00	80.00	125.00	650.00
☐ 1902	Lyons-Treat	Red	50.00	90.00	125.00	675.00
☐ 1902	Vernon-Treat	Red	50.00	100.00	125.00	725.00

$10.00

Back Design: Same as Note No. 70, date 1902-1908.
Face Design: Same as Note No. 71.

Second Issue—blue seal and numbers, 1902-1908 on the back.

SERIES	SIGNATURES	SEAL	A.B.P.	GOOD	V. FINE	UNC.
☐1902	Lyons-Roberts	Blue	30.00	40.00	65.00	325.00
☐1902	Lyons-Treat	Blue	30.00	40.00	65.00	325.00
☐1902	Vernon-Treat	Blue	30.00	40.00	65.00	325.00
☐1902	Vernon-McClung	Blue	30.00	40.00	65.00	325.00
☐1902	Napier-McClung	Blue	30.00	40.00	65.00	325.00
☐1902	Napier-Thompson	Blue	30.00	55.00	100.00	350.00
☐1902	Napier-Burke	Blue	30.00	40.00	75.00	325.00
☐1902	Parker-Burke	Blue	30.00	40.00	75.00	325.00
☐1902	Teehee-Burke	Blue	30.00	50.00	150.00	400.00

Third Issue—blue seal and numbers, without date on back.

SERIES	SIGNATURES	SEAL	A.B.P.	GOOD	V. FINE	UNC.
☐1902	Lyons-Roberts	Blue	20.00	40.00	75.00	280.00
☐1902	Lyons-Treat	Blue	20.00	40.00	75.00	280.00
☐1902	Vernon-Treat	Blue	20.00	40.00	75.00	280.00
☐1902	Vernon-McClung	Blue	20.00	40.00	75.00	280.00
☐1902	Napier-McClung	Blue	20.00	40.00	75.00	280.00
☐1902	Napier-Thompson	Blue	20.00	45.00	100.00	300.00
☐1902	Napier-Burke	Blue	20.00	40.00	75.00	280.00
☐1902	Parker-Burke	Blue	20.00	40.00	75.00	280.00
☐1902	Teehee-Burke	Blue	20.00	40.00	75.00	280.00
☐1902	Elliott-Burke	Blue	20.00	40.00	75.00	280.00
☐1902	Elliott-White	Blue	20.00	40.00	75.00	280.00
☐1902	Speelman-White	Blue	20.00	40.00	75.00	280.00
☐1902	Woods-White	Blue	20.00	35.00	85.00	285.00
☐1902	Woods-Tate	Blue	20.00	40.00	85.00	290.00
☐1902	Jones-Woods	Blue	55.00	110.00	400.00	1200.00

Face Design—TYPE I: Portrait of Hamilton center, name of Bank left, brown seal right, Charter number black.

Face Design—TYPE II: Charter number added in brown.

Back Design: United States Treasury Building.

SERIES	SIGNATURES	SEAL	A.B.P.	GOOD	V. FINE	UNC.
☐1929—TYPE I	Jones-Woods	Brown	12.00	18.00	25.00	65.00
☐1929—TYPE II	Jones-Woods	Brown	14.00	22.00	30.00	80.00

Face Design: Similar to Note No. 66

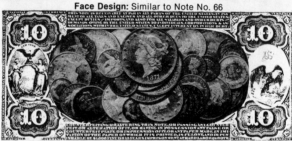

Back Design: State Seal left, gold coins center, American Eagle right.

SIGNATURES OF ALLISON-SPINNER, RED TREASURY SEAL

SERIES	NAME OF BANK	CITY	A.B.P.	GOOD	V. GOOD
☐ 1870	First National Gold Bank	San Francisco	325.00	600.00	2500.00
☐ 1872	National Gold Bank and Trust Company	San Francisco	310.00	550.00	2000.00
☐ 1872	National Gold Bank of D.O. Mills and Company	Sacramento	280.00	600.00	2500.00
☐ 1873	First National Gold Bank	Santa Barbara	300.00	550.00	2500.00
☐ 1873	First National Gold Bank	Stockton	300.00	550.00	2500.00
☐ 1874	Farmers Nat'l Gold Bank	San Jose	300.00	550.00	2500.00
☐ 1874	First National Gold Bank	Petaluma	300.00	550.00	2500.00
☐ 1875	First National Gold Bank	Oakland	300.00	600.00	2500.00

Face Design: Portrait of Robert Morris left.

$10.00

Back Design: Printed in black ink, large letters "SILVER".

SERIES	SIGNATURES	SEAL	A.B.P.	GOOD	V. FINE	UNC.
☐1880	Scofield-Gilfillan	Brown	115.00	165.00	850.00	4500.00
☐1880	Bruce-Gilfillan	Brown	115.00	165.00	850.00	4500.00
☐1880	Bruce-Wyman	Brown	115.00	165.00	850.00	4500.00
☐1880	Bruce-Wyman	Red	125.00	260.00	1300.00	5500.00

TEN DOLLAR NOTES (1886) SILVER CERTIFICATES
(Large Size)

Face Design: Portrait of Thomas A. Hendricks in center.

Back Design

SERIES	SIGNATURES	SEAL	A.B.P.	GOOD	V. FINE	UNC.
☐ 1886	Rosecrans-Jordan	Small Red	50.00	135.00	475.00	4000.00
☐ 1886	Rosecrans-Hyatt	Small Red	50.00	135.00	475.00	4000.00
☐ 1886	Rosecrans-Hyatt	Large Red	50.00	135.00	475.00	3600.00
☐ 1886	Rosecrans-Huston	Large Red	50.00	135.00	475.00	3600.00
☐ 1886	Rosecrans-Huston	Large Brown	50.00	130.00	450.00	3250.00
☐ 1886	Rosecrans-Nebeker	Large Brown	50.00	130.00	450.00	3250.00
☐ 1886	Rosecrans-Nebeker	Small Red	55.00	140.00	500.00	4500.00

TEN DOLLAR NOTES (1891-1908) SILVER CERTIFICATES
(Large Size)
NOTE NO. 75

Face Design: Same as Note No. 74.

Back Design

SERIES	SIGNATURES	SEAL	A.B.P.	GOOD	V. FINE	UNC.
☐ 1891	Rosecrans-Nebeker	Red	30.00	70.00	250.00	2500.00
☐ 1891	Tillman-Morgan	Red	30.00	70.00	250.00	2500.00
☐ 1891	Bruce-Roberts	Red	30.00	70.00	250.00	2500.00
☐ 1891	Lyons-Roberts	Red	30.00	70.00	250.00	2500.00
☐ 1891	Vernon-Treat	Blue	30.00	70.00	250.00	2600.00
☐ 1891	Vernon-McClung	Blue	30.00	70.00	250.00	2600.00
☐ 1891	Parker-Burke	Blue	30.00	70.00	250.00	2600.00

TEN DOLLAR NOTES (1933) SILVER CERTIFICATES
(Small Size)

Face Design: Portrait of President Hamilton, center. Blue seal to left, blue numbers.

Back Design: Green United States Treasury Building.

SERIES	SIGNATURES	SEAL	A.B.P.	GOOD	V. FINE	UNC.
☐ 1933	Julian-Woodin	Blue	350.00	525.00	750.00	3500.00

TEN DOLLAR NOTES (1934) SILVER CERTIFICATES
(Small Size)

Face Design: Blue "10" to left of portrait. Treasury Seal is now to right.

Back Design: Similar to previous issue.

TEN DOLLAR NOTES (1934) SILVER CERTIFICATES
(Small Size)

SERIES	SIGNATURES	SEAL	A.B.P.	GOOD	V. FINE	UNC.
☐1934	Julian-Morgenthau	Blue	11.50	15.00	20.00	45.00
☐1934	Julian-Morgenthau*	Yellow	100.00	200.00	750.00	3000.00
☐1934A	Julian-Morgenthau	Blue	11.50	15.00	20.00	47.50
☐1934A	Julian-Morgenthau*	Yellow	14.00	18.00	30.00	135.00
☐1934B	Julian-Vinson	Blue	25.00	40.00	110.00	800.00
☐1934C	Julian-Snyder	Blue	11.50	14.00	18.00	32.50
☐1934D	Clark-Snyder	Blue	11.50	14.00	18.00	30.00

NOTE: *Silver Certificates with a yellow seal were a special issue for use in combat areas of North Africa and Europe during World War II.

TEN DOLLAR NOTES (1953) SILVER CERTIFICATES
(Small Size)

Face Design: Gray "10" to left of portrait, Treasury Seal is smaller.
Back Design: Back similar to previous note.

SERIES	SIGNATURES	SEAL	A.B.P.	GOOD	V. FINE	UNC.
☐1953	Priest-Humphrey	Blue	11.00	——	15.00	40.00
☐1953A	Priest-Anderson	Blue	11.00	——	15.00	50.00
☐1953B	Smith-Dillon	Blue	11.00	——	20.00	45.00

ABOVE NOTE ONLY 720,000 ISSUED

NOTE: Last issue of $10.00 Silver Certificates. These were not issued with "In God We Trust" on the back. Production ended in 1962.

TEN DOLLAR (1879) REFUNDING CERTIFICATE

Face Design: Portrait of Franklin.

Back Design: Large "TEN", ornate cornucopia border.

SERIES	SIGNATURES	SEAL	A.B.P.	V. FINE	UNC.
☐ 1879	Scofield-Gilfillan	Red	550.00	2250.00	10000.00

$10.00

Face Design: Portrait of Hillegas center, yellow "X" left, yellow seal right, yellow numbers.

Back Design: The backs are a bright yellow color.

SERIES	SIGNATURES	SEAL	A.B.P.	GOOD	V. FINE	UNC.
☐ 1907	Vernon-Treat	Gold	14.00	25.00	70.00	500.00
☐ 1907	Vernon-McClung	Gold	14.00	25.00	70.00	500.00
☐ 1907	Napier-McClung	Gold	14.00	25.00	70.00	500.00
☐ 1907	Napier-Thompson	Gold	18.00	35.00	95.00	675.00
☐ 1907	Parker-Burke	Gold	14.00	25.00	70.00	500.00
☐ 1907	Teehee-Burke	Gold	14.00	25.00	70.00	500.00
☐ 1922	Speelman-White	Gold	14.00	25.00	65.00	475.00

TEN DOLLAR NOTES (1928) GOLD CERTIFICATES

(Small Size)

Face Design: Portrait of Alexander Hamilton center, yellow seal to left, yellow numbers.

Back Design: Printed in green ink.

SERIES	SIGNATURES	SEAL	A.B.P.	GOOD	V. FINE	UNC.
☐1928	Woods-Mellon	Gold	12.50	18.00	45.00	175.00

$10.00

TEN DOLLAR NOTES (1890) TREASURY NOTES

(Large Size)

Face Design: Portrait of General Philip Sheridan.

Back Design:
Very ornate
large "TEN."

SERIES	SIGNATURES	SEAL	A.B.P.	GOOD	V. FINE	UNC.
☐1890	Rosecrans-Huston	Lg. Brown	85.00	150.00	550.00	3500.00
☐1890	Rosecrans-Nebeker	Lg. Brown	85.00	150.00	550.00	3500.00
☐1890	Rosecrans-Nebeker	Sm. Red	85.00	150.00	550.00	3500.00

TEN DOLLAR NOTES (1891) TREASURY NOTES

(Large Size)
NOTE NO. 81A

Face Design:
Same as No. 81
Back Design:
Ornate small
"TEN."

SERIES	SIGNATURES	SEAL	A.B.P.	GOOD	V. FINE	UNC.
☐1891	Rosecrans-Nebeker	Sm. Red	52.50	100.00	275.00	1400.00
☐1891	Tillman-Morgan	Sm. Red	52.50	100.00	275.00	1400.00
☐1891	Bruce-Roberts	Sm. Red	52.50	100.00	275.00	1400.00

Face Design: Portrait of President Jackson center, Federal Reserve Seal left, Treasury Seal right.

Back Design: Scenes of farming and industry.
SIGNATURES OF BURKE-McADOO, RED SEALS AND RED SERIAL NUMBERS

SERIES	CITY	SEAL	A.B.P.	GOOD	V. FINE	UNC.
☐1914	Boston	Red	25.00	40.00	90.00	750.00
☐1914	New York	Red	20.00	35.00	75.00	700.00
☐1914	Philadelphia	Red	20.00	35.00	75.00	700.00
☐1914	Cleveland	Red	20.00	35.00	75.00	700.00
☐1914	Richmond	Red	20.00	35.00	75.00	700.00
☐1914	Atlanta	Red	20.00	35.00	75.00	700.00
☐1914	Chicago	Red	20.00	35.00	75.00	700.00
☐1914	St. Louis	Red	20.00	35.00	75.00	700.00
☐1914	Minneapolis	Red	20.00	35.00	75.00	700.00
☐1914	Kansas City	Red	20.00	35.00	75.00	700.00
☐1914	Dallas	Red	20.00	35.00	90.00	750.00
☐1914	San Francisco	Red	20.00	35.00	90.00	750.00

$10.00

TEN DOLLAR NOTES (1914) FEDERAL RESERVE NOTES
(Large Size)

BANK & CITY	SIGNATURES	SEAL	A.B.P.	V. FINE	UNC.
☐Boston	Burke-McAdoo	Blue	15.00	30.00	225.00
☐Boston	Burke-Glass	Blue	20.00	40.00	240.00
☐Boston	Burke-Huston	Blue	15.00	30.00	225.00
☐Boston	White-Mellon	Blue	15.00	30.00	225.00
☐New York	Burke-McAdoo	Blue	15.00	30.00	225.00
☐New York	Burke-Glass	Blue	20.00	40.00	240.00
☐New York	Burke-Huston	Blue	15.00	30.00	225.00
☐New York	White-Mellon	Blue	15.00	30.00	225.00
☐Philadelphia	Burke-McAdoo	Blue	15.00	30.00	225.00
☐Philadelphia	Burke-Glass	Blue	15.00	30.00	225.00
☐Philadelphia	Burke-Huston	Blue	15.00	30.00	225.00
☐Philadelphia	White-Mellon	Blue	15.00	30.00	225.00
☐Cleveland	Burke-McAdoo	Blue	15.00	30.00	225.00
☐Cleveland	Burke-Glass	Blue	15.00	30.00	225.00
☐Cleveland	Burke-Huston	Blue	15.00	30.00	225.00
☐Cleveland	White-Mellon	Blue	15.00	30.00	225.00
☐Richmond	Burke-McAdoo	Blue	15.00	30.00	225.00
☐Richmond	Burke-Glass	Blue	15.00	30.00	225.00
☐Richmond	Burke-Huston	Blue	15.00	30.00	225.00
☐Richmond	White-Mellon	Blue	15.00	30.00	225.00
☐Atlanta	Burke-McAdoo	Blue	15.00	30.00	225.00
☐Atlanta	Burke-Glass	Blue	20.00	40.00	240.00
☐Atlanta	Burke-Huston	Blue	15.00	30.00	225.00
☐Atlanta	White-Mellon	Blue	15.00	30.00	225.00
☐Chicago	Burke-McAdoo	Blue	15.00	30.00	225.00
☐Chicago	Burke-Glass	Blue	15.00	30.00	225.00
☐Chicago	Burke-Huston	Blue	15.00	30.00	225.00
☐Chicago	White-Mellon	Blue	15.00	30.00	225.00
☐St. Louis	Burke-McAdoo	Blue	15.00	30.00	225.00
☐St. Louis	Burke-Glass	Blue	15.00	30.00	225.00
☐St. Louis	Burke-Huston	Blue	15.00	30.00	225.00
☐St. Louis	White-Mellon	Blue	15.00	30.00	225.00
☐Minneapolis	Burke-McAdoo	Blue	15.00	30.00	225.00
☐Minneapolis	Burke-Glass	Blue	15.00	30.00	225.00
☐Minneapolis	Burke-Huston	Blue	15.00	30.00	225.00
☐Minneapolis	White-Mellon	Blue	15.00	30.00	225.00
☐Kansas City	Burke-McAdoo	Blue	15.00	30.00	225.00
☐Kansas City	Burke-Glass	Blue	20.00	40.00	240.00
☐Kansas City	Burke-Huston	Blue	15.00	30.00	225.00
☐Kansas City	White-Mellon	Blue	15.00	30.00	225.00
☐Dallas	Burke-McAdoo	Blue	15.00	30.00	225.00
☐Dallas	Burke-Glass	Blue	15.00	30.00	225.00
☐Dallas	Burke-Huston	Blue	15.00	30.00	225.00
☐Dallas	White-Mellon	Blue	15.00	30.00	225.00
☐San Francisco	Burke-McAdoo	Blue	15.00	30.00	225.00
☐San Francisco	Burke-Glass	Blue	20.00	40.00	240.00
☐San Francisco	Burke-Huston	Blue	15.00	30.00	225.00
☐San Francisco	White-Mellon	Blue	15.00	30.00	225.00

TEN DOLLAR NOTES (1928-1928A) FEDERAL RESERVE NOTES
(Small Size)

Face Design: Portrait of Alexander Hamilton center, black Federal Reserve Seal left, with number, green Treasury Seal to the right.

Back Design: United States Treasury Building.

SERIES OF 1928 — SIGNATURES OF TATE-MELLON, GREEN SEAL

BANK & CITY	A.B.P.	V.FINE	UNC.	BANK & CITY	A.B.P.	V.FINE	UNC.
☐Boston	12.00	22.50	45.00	☐Chicago	14.00	22.50	45.00
☐New York	12.00	22.50	45.00	☐St. Louis	14.00	22.50	52.50
☐Philadelphia	12.00	22.50	45.00	☐Minneapolis	14.00	25.00	52.50
☐Cleveland	12.50	25.00	45.00	☐Kansas City	14.00	25.00	52.50
☐Richmond	12.50	25.00	48.00	☐Dallas	15.00	30.00	52.50
☐Atlanta	14.00	30.00	48.00	☐San Francisco	14.00	22.50	45.00

SERIES OF 1928A — SIGNATURES OF WOODS-MELLON, GREEN SEAL

BANK & CITY	A.B.P.	V.FINE	UNC.	BANK & CITY	A.B.P.	V.FINE	UNC.
☐Boston	12.00	20.00	35.00	☐Chicago	14.00	25.00	40.00
☐New York	12.00	20.00	40.00	☐St. Louis	18.00	35.00	70.00
☐Philadelphia	12.00	20.00	40.00	☐Minneapolis	18.00	35.00	80.00
☐Cleveland	12.00	22.50	40.00	☐Kansas City	18.00	35.00	65.00
☐Richmond	12.50	25.00	50.00	☐Dallas	18.00	35.00	65.00
☐Atlanta	14.00	30.00	45.00	☐San Francisco	18.00	35.00	45.00

$10.00

TEN DOLLAR NOTES (1928B-1928C) FEDERAL RESERVE NOTES
(Small Issue)

NOTE NO. 83A

Face Design: Alexander Hamilton black Federal Reserve Seal left has letter instead of number.

Back Design: Same as Note No. 83.

SERIES OF 1928B — SIGNATURES OF WOODS-MELLON, GREEN SEAL

BANK & CITY	A.B.P.	V.FINE	UNC.	BANK & CITY	A.B.P.	V.FINE	UNC.
☐Boston	12.00	20.00	32.50	☐Chicago	14.00	25.00	32.50
☐New York	12.00	20.00	32.50	☐St. Louis	14.00	25.00	32.50
☐Philadelphia	12.00	20.00	32.50	☐Minneapolis	14.00	25.00	32.50
☐Cleveland	12.00	22.50	32.50	☐Kansas City	14.00	25.00	32.50
☐Richmond	12.50	25.00	32.50	☐Dallas	14.00	25.00	40.00
☐Atlanta	12.50	25.00	32.50	☐San Francisco	14.00	25.00	30.00

SERIES OF 1928C — SIGNATURES OF WOODS-MILLS, GREEN SEAL

BANK & CITY	A.B.P.	V.FINE	UNC.	BANK & CITY	A.B.P.	V.FINE	UNC.
☐New York	20.00	35.00	100.00	☐Atlanta	20.00	35.00	100.00
☐Cleveland	20.00	35.00	100.00	☐Chicago	20.00	35.00	100.00
☐Richmond	20.00	35.00	100.00				

TEN DOLLAR NOTES (1934) FEDERAL RESERVE NOTES
(Small Size)

NOTE NO. 83B

SERIES OF 1934 — SIGNATURES OF JULIAN-MORGENTHAU, GREEN SEAL

BANK & CITY	A.B.P.	V.FINE	UNC.	BANK & CITY	A.B.P.	V.FINE	UNC.
☐Boston	12.00	17.00	30.00	☐Chicago	12.00	14.50	22.50
☐New York	11.50	15.00	22.50	☐St. Louis	12.00	17.00	27.50
☐Philadelphia	12.00	15.00	25.00	☐Minneapolis	12.50	17.00	30.00
☐Cleveland	12.50	15.00	25.00	☐Kansas City	12.00	17.00	30.00
☐Richmond	12.50	16.00	27.50	☐Dallas	12.00	17.00	30.00
☐Atlanta	12.50	16.00	27.50	☐San Francisco	12.00	16.00	28.00

NOTE: The green Treasury Seal on this note is known in a light and dark color. The light seal is worth about 10% to 20% more in most cases. ''Redeemable In Gold'' removed from obligation over Federal Reserve Seal.

TEN DOLLAR NOTES (1934) FEDERAL RESERVE NOTES
(Small Size)

SERIES OF 1934A—SIGNATURES OF JULIAN-MORGENTHAU, GREEN SEAL

BANK & CITY	A.B.P.	V.FINE	UNC.	BANK & CITY	A.B.P.	V.FINE	UNC.
☐Boston	11.50	16.00	25.00	☐Chicago	11.50	16.00	25.00
☐New York	11.50	16.00	25.00	☐St. Louis	11.50	16.00	32.50
☐Philadelphia	11.50	16.00	25.00	☐Minneapolis	11.50	16.00	35.00
☐Cleveland	11.50	16.00	27.50	☐Kansas City	11.50	16.00	27.40
☐Richmond	11.50	16.00	28.00	☐Dallas	11.50	16.00	27.50
☐Atlanta	11.50	16.00	28.00	☐San Francisco*	18.00	32.00	60.00

*San Francisco - 1934A with brown seal and overprinted HAWAII on face and back. Special issue for use in combat areas during World War II. Value in V. Fine $45.00, Value in Unc. $220.00.

SERIES OF 1934B — SIGNATURES OF JULIAN-VINSON, GREEN SEAL

BANK & CITY	A.B.P.	V.FINE	UNC.	BANK & CITY	A.B.P.	V.FINE	UNC.
☐Boston	11.50	17.50	30.00	☐Chicago	11.50	17.50	30.00
☐New York	11.50	17.50	30.00	☐St. Louis	11.50	17.50	30.00
☐Philadelphia	11.50	17.50	30.00	☐Minneapolis	11.50	17.50	30.00
☐Cleveland	11.50	17.50	32.50	☐Kansas City	11.50	17.50	30.00
☐Richmond	11.50	17.50	30.00	☐Dallas	11.50	17.50	32.50
☐Atlanta	11.50	17.50	30.00	☐San Francisco	11.50	17.50	30.00

SERIES OF 1934C — SIGNATURES OF JULIAN-SNYDER, GREEN SEAL

BANK & CITY	A.B.P.	V.FINE	UNC.	BANK & CITY	A.B.P.	V.FINE	UNC.
☐Boston	11.50	14.00	25.00	☐Chicago	11.50	14.00	22.50
☐New York	11.50	14.00	22.50	☐St. Louis	11.50	14.00	25.00
☐Philadelphia	11.50	14.00	22.50	☐Minneapolis	11.50	14.00	30.00
☐Cleveland	11.50	30.00	85.00	☐Kansas City	11.50	14.00	30.00
☐Richmond	11.50	14.00	25.00	☐Dallas	11.50	14.00	25.00
☐Atlanta	11.50	14.00	25.00	☐San Francisco	11.50	14.00	25.00

SERIES OF 1934D — SIGNATURES OF CLARK-SNYDER, GREEN SEAL

BANK & CITY	A.B.P.	V.FINE	UNC.	BANK & CITY	A.B.P.	V.FINE	UNC.
☐Boston	11.50	14.00	25.00	☐Chicago	11.50	14.00	25.00
☐New York	11.50	14.00	25.00	☐St. Louis	11.50	14.00	25.00
☐Philadelphia	11.50	14.00	25.00	☐Minneapolis	11.50	14.00	30.00
☐Cleveland	11.50	14.00	27.50	☐Kansas City	11.50	14.00	32.50
☐Richmond	11.50	14.00	25.00	☐Dallas	11.50	14.00	30.00
☐Atlanta	11.50	14.00	25.00	☐San Francisco	11.50	14.00	27.50

TEN DOLLAR NOTES (1950) FEDERAL RESERVE NOTES
(Small Size)   **NOTE NO.83CC**

SERIES OF 1950 — CLARK-SNYDER SIGNATURES, GREEN SEAL
                                                               UNC.
Issued for all Federal Reserve Banks 22.50

SERIES OF 1950A — SIGNATURES OF PRIEST-HUMPHREY, GREEN SEAL
Issued for all Federal Reserve Bank 20.00

SERIES OF 1950B — SIGNATURES OF PRIEST-ANDERSON, GREEN SEAL
Issued for all Federal Reserve Banks 18.50

SERIES OF 1950C — SIGNATURES OF SMITH-DILLON, GREEN SEAL
Issued for all Federal Reserve Banks 17.50

SERIES OF 1950D — SIGNATURES OF GRANAHAN-DILLON, GREEN SEAL
Issued for all Federal Reserve Banks 17.50

SERIES OF 1950E — SIGNATURES OF GRANAHAN-FOWLER, GREEN SEAL

BANK	UNC.	BANK	UNC.
☐ New York	20.00	☐ San Francisco	22.00
☐ Chicago	20.00	ONLY DISTRICTS USED	

TEN DOLLAR NOTES (1963) FEDERAL RESERVE NOTES
(Small Size)   ("IN GOD WE TRUST" ADDED ON BACK)   **NOTE NO.83D**

SERIES OF 1963 — SIGNATURES OF GRANAHAN-DILLON, GREEN SEAL
Issued for all banks except Minneapolis . . . . .Average Price is 17.50

SERIES OF 1963A — SIGNATURES OF GRANAHAN-FOWLER, GREEN SEAL
Issued for all Federal Reserve Banks . . . . .Average Price is 17.00

TEN DOLLAR NOTES (1969) FEDERAL RESERVE NOTES
(WORDING IN GREEN TREASURY SEAL CHANGED FROM LATIN TO ENGLISH)
(Small Size)   **NOTE NO.83E**

SERIES OF 1969 — SIGNATURES OF ELSTON-KENNEDY
Issued for all Federal Reserve Banks 15.00

SERIES OF 1969A — SIGNATURES OF KABIS-CONNALLY
Issued for all Federal Reserve Banks 14.00

SERIES OF 1969B — SIGNATURES OF BANUELOS-CONNALLY
Issued for all Federal Reserve Banks 13.50

SERIES OF 1969C — SIGNATURES OF BANUELOS-SHULTZ
Issued for all Federal Reserve Banks 12.50

SERIES OF 1974 — SIGNATURES OF NEFF-SIMON
Issued for all Federal Reserve Banks 11.50

SERIES OF 1977 — SIGNATURES OF MORTON-BLUMENTHAL
Issued for all Federal Reserve Banks 11.00

SERIES OF 1977A — SIGNATURES OF MORTON-MILLER
Issued for all Federal Reserve Banks . . . . .CURRENT

TEN DOLLAR NOTES (1915-1918) FEDERAL RESERVE BANK
(Large Size)

Face Design: Portrait of President Jackson to left, Bank and City in center, blue seal to the right.

Back Design: Similar to Note No. 82.

BANK & CITY	GOVERNMENT SERIES	SIGNATURES	BANK SIGNATURES	A.B.P.	GOOD	V. FINE	UNC.
☐ New York	1918	Teehee-Burke	Hendricks-Strong	60.00	100.00	300.00	1600.00
☐ Atlanta	1915	Teehee-Burke	Bell-Wellborn	75.00	150.00	350.00	1600.00
☐ Atlanta	1918	Elliott-Burke	Bell-Wellborn	60.00	100.00	300.00	1600.00
☐ Chicago	1915	Teehee-Burke	McLallen-McDougal	40.00	75.00	300.00	1500.00
☐ Chicago	1918	Teehee-Burke	McCloud-McDougal	40.00	75.00	300.00	1600.00
☐ St. Louis	1918	Teehee-Burke	Attebery-Wells	75.00	150.00	350.00	1600.00
☐ Kan. City	1915	Teehee-Burke	Anderson-Miller	35.00	50.00	300.00	1500.00
☐ Kan. City	1915	Teehee-Burke	Cross-Miller	35.00	50.00	300.00	1500.00
☐ Kan. City	1915	Teehee-Burke	Helm-Miller	35.00	50.00	300.00	1500.00
☐ Dallas	1915	Teehee-Burke	Hoopes-VanZandt	40.00	75.00	300.00	1500.00
☐ Dallas	1915	Teehee-Burke	Gilbert-VanZandt	75.00	150.00	400.00	1600.00
☐ Dallas	1915	Teehee-Burke	Talley-VanZandt	40.00	75.00	300.00	1500.00

$10.00

TEN DOLLAR NOTES (1929) FEDERAL RESERVE BANK NOTES
(Small Size)

Face Design: Portrait of Hamilton.

Back Design: Same as all small size $10.00 Notes.

SIGNATURES OF JONES-WOODS, BROWN SEAL

BANK	SEAL	A.B.P.	GOOD	V. FINE	UNC.
☐ Boston	Brown	12.00	20.00	30.00	50.00
☐ New York	Brown	12.00	20.00	30.00	45.00
☐ Philadelphia	Brown	12.00	20.00	30.00	55.00
☐ Cleveland	Brown	12.00	20.00	30.00	45.00
☐ Richmond	Brown	12.00	20.00	30.00	50.00
☐ Atlanta	Brown	12.00	18.00	30.00	60.00
☐ Chicago	Brown	16.00	24.00	30.00	40.00
☐ St. Louis	Brown	16.00	24.00	35.00	50.00
☐ Minneapolis	Brown	16.00	24.00	35.00	75.00
☐ Kansas City	Brown	16.00	24.00	35.00	70.00
☐ Dallas	Brown	16.00	24.00	35.00	150.00
☐ San Francisco	Brown	16.00	24.00	35.00	75.00

TWENTY DOLLAR NOTES

ORDER OF ISSUE

$20.00

Face Design: Liberty with sword and shield.

Back Design: Intricate design of numerals "20", Demand
Notes have no Treasury Seal.

SERIES	PAYABLE AT	A.B.P.	GOOD	V.GOOD
☐1861	Boston (I)	3250.00	4200.00	8000.00
☐1861	New York (I)	3250.00	4200.00	8000.00
☐1861	Philadelphia (I)	3250.00	4200.00	8000.00
☐1861	Cincinnati (I)	3500.00	4800.00	8000.00
☐1861	St. Louis (I)	(Unknown in any collection)		
☐1861	Boston (II)	3250.00	4200.00	7000.00
☐1861	New York (II)	3250.00	4200.00	7000.00
☐1861	Philadelphia (II)	3250.00	4200.00	7000.00
☐1861	Cincinnati (II)	3250.00	4200.00	7000.00
☐1861	St. Louis (II)	(Unknown in any collection)		

*NOTE: Counterfeits and expertly repaired specimens exist. Use caution in buying.

TWENTY DOLLAR NOTES (1862-1863) UNITED STATES NOTES
(ALSO KNOWN AS LEGAL TENDER NOTES)

(Large Size)

Face Design: Liberty with sword and shield

Back Design: Second obligation. This Note was also issued with first obligation on the back. See Notes No. 33 and 33A.

SERIES	SIGNATURES	SEAL	A.B.P.	GOOD	V. FINE	UNC.
☐ 1862	Chittenden-Spinner*	Red	75.00	165.00	550.00	3000.00
☐ 1862	Chittenden-Spinner**	Red	75.00	165.00	550.00	3000.00
☐ 1863	Chittenden-Spinner**	Red	75.00	165.00	550.00	3000.00

*First Obligation: Similar to Note No. 33   **Second Obligation: Shown above.

TWENTY DOLLAR NOTES (1869) UNITED STATES NOTES
(ALSO KNOWN AS LEGAL TENDER NOTES)

(Large Size)

Face Design

Back Design: No. 87A revised.

Back Design: No. 87.

87 SERIES SIGNATURES	SEAL	A.B.P.	GOOD	V. FINE	UNC.
☐1869 Allison-Spinner	Red	125.00	475.00	1000.00	4500.00

87A SERIES Back Design: Revised

☐1875 Allison-New	Red	50.00	100.00	400.00	2100.00
☐1878 Allison-Gilfillan	Red	50.00	100.00	400.00	2100.00
☐1880 Scofield-Gilfillan	Brown Lg.	40.00	75.00	275.00	1600.00
☐1880 Bruce-Gilfillan	Brown Lg.	40.00	75.00	275.00	1600.00
☐1880 Bruce-Wyman	Brown Lg.	40.00	75.00	275.00	1600.00
☐1880 Bruce-Wyman	Red Lg.	40.00	75.00	275.00	1600.00
☐1880 Rosecrans-Jordan	Red Lg.	40.00	75.00	275.00	1600.00
☐1880 Rosecrans-Hyatt	Red Plain	40.00	75.00	275.00	1600.00
☐1880 Rosecrans-Hyatt	Red Spikes	40.00	75.00	250.00	1600.00
☐1880 Rosecrans-Huston	Red Lg.	40.00	75.00	250.00	1600.00
☐1880 Rosecrans-Huston	Brown Lg.	40.00	75.00	250.00	1600.00
☐1880 Rosecrans-Nebeker	Brown Lg.	40.00	75.00	250.00	1600.00
☐1880 Rosecrans-Nebeker	Red Sm.	40.00	75.00	225.00	1400.00
☐1880 Tillman-Morgan	Red Sm.	40.00	75.00	225.00	1400.00
☐1880 Bruce-Roberts	Red Sm.	40.00	75.00	225.00	1400.00
☐1880 Lyons-Roberts	Red Sm.	40.00	75.00	225.00	1400.00
☐1880 Vernon-Treat	Red Sm.	40.00	75.00	225.00	1400.00
☐1880 Vernon-McClung	Red Sm.	40.00	75.00	225.00	1400.00
☐1880 Teehee-Burke	Red Sm.	40.00	75.00	225.00	1400.00
☐1880 Elliott-White	Red Sm.	40.00	75.00	225.00	1400.00

TWENTY DOLLAR NOTES (1863-1875) NATIONAL BANK NOTE
FIRST CHARTER PERIOD (Large Size)

NOTE NO. 88

Face Design: Battle of Lexington left, name of Bank in center. Columbia with flag right.

Back Design: Green border, black center picture of baptism of Pocahontas.

SERIES	SIGNATURES	SEAL	A.B.P.	GOOD	V. FINE	UNC.
☐Original	Chittenden-Spinner	Red	100.00	175.00	600.00	3750.00
☐Original	Colby-Spinner	Red	100.00	175.00	625.00	4000.00
☐Original	Jeffries-Spinner	Red	400.00	1250.00	4750.00	
☐Original	Allison-Spinner	Red	100.00	175.00	600.00	3750.00
☐1875	Allison-New	Red	100.00	175.00	600.00	4250.00
☐1875	Allison-Wyman	Red	100.00	175.00	600.00	4250.00
☐1875	Allison-Gilfillan	Red	100.00	175.00	600.00	4250.00
☐1875	Scofield-Gilfillan	Red	100.00	175.00	600.00	4250.00
☐1875	Bruce-Gilfillan	Red	100.00	175.00	600.00	4250.00
☐1875	Bruce-Wyman	Red	100.00	175.00	600.00	4250.00
☐1875	Rosecrans-Huston	Red	100.00	175.00	600.00	4250.00
☐1875	Rosecrans-Nebeker	Red	100.00	175.00	600.00	4250.00
☐1875	Tillman-Morgan	Red	100.00	175.00	600.00	4250.00

$20.00

TWENTY DOLLAR NOTES (1882) NATIONAL BANK NOTES

SECOND CHARTER PERIOD (Large Size)   NOTE NO. 88A

First Issue—brown seal and brown backs.

Face Design: Similar to Note No. 88.
Back Design: Similar to Note No. 39, border is brown, green Charter number in center.

SERIES	SIGNATURES	SEAL	A.B.P.	GOOD	V. FINE	UNC.
☐1882	Bruce-Gilfillan	Brown	50.00	100.00	200.00	800.00
☐1882	Bruce-Wyman	Brown	50.00	100.00	200.00	800.00
☐1882	Bruce-Jordan	Brown	50.00	100.00	200.00	1000.00
☐1882	Rosecrans-Jordan	Brown	50.00	100.00	200.00	875.00
☐1882	Rosecrans-Hyatt	Brown	50.00	100.00	200.00	875.00
☐1882	Rosecrans-Huston	Brown	50.00	100.00	200.00	875.00
☐1882	Rosecrans-Nebeker	Brown	50.00	100.00	200.00	875.00
☐1882	Rosecrans-Morgan	Brown	125.00	300.00	800.00	4500.00
☐1882	Tillman-Morgan	Brown	50.00	100.00	200.00	800.00
☐1882	Tillman-Roberts	Brown	50.00	100.00	200.00	800.00
☐1882	Bruce-Roberts	Brown	50.00	100.00	200.00	800.00
☐1882	Lyons-Roberts	Brown	50.00	100.00	200.00	800.00
☐1882	Lyons-Treat	Brown	50.00	100.00	200.00	1350.00
☐1882	Vernon-Treat	Brown	50.00	100.00	200.00	1350.00

SECOND CHARTER PERIOD, Second Issue (Large Size)   NOTE NO. 88B

Face Design: Similar to Note No. 88 **Back Design:** Similar to Note No. 40.

SERIES	SIGNATURES	SEAL	A.B.P.	GOOD	V. FINE	UNC.
☐1882	Rosecrans-Huston	Blue	70.00	125.00	200.00	1200.00
☐1882	Rosecrans-Nebeker	Blue	70.00	125.00	200.00	1100.00
☐1882	Rosecrans-Morgan	Blue	130.00	300.00	850.00	4750.00
☐1882	Tillman-Morgan	Blue	70.00	125.00	200.00	1100.00
☐1882	Tillman-Roberts	Blue	70.00	125.00	200.00	1100.00
☐1882	Bruce-Roberts	Blue	70.00	125.00	200.00	1300.00
☐1882	Lyons-Roberts	Blue	70.00	125.00	200.00	1100.00
☐1882	Vernon-Treat	Blue	70.00	125.00	200.00	1300.00
☐1882	Napier-McClung	Blue	70.00	125.00	200.00	1475.00

SECOND CHARTER PERIOD, Third Issue (Large Size)   NOTE NO. 88C

Face Design: Similar to Note No. 88 with blue seal.
Back Design: Similar to Note No. 41, green back, value in block letters.

SERIES	SIGNATURES	SEAL	A.B.P.	GOOD	V. FINE	UNC.
☐1882	Tillman-Morgan	Blue	90.00	175.00	500.00	2750.00
☐1882	Lyons-Roberts	Blue	90.00	175.00	500.00	2750.00
☐1882	Lyons-Treat	Blue	90.00	175.00	500.00	2750.00
☐1882	Vernon-Treat	Blue	90.00	175.00	500.00	2750.00
☐1882	Napier-McClung	Blue	90.00	175.00	500.00	2750.00
☐1882	Teehee-Burke	Blue	90.00	175.00	500.00	2750.00

Face Design: Portrait of McCulloch left, name of bank center, Treasury Seal right.

SERIES	SIGNATURES	SEAL	A.B.P.	GOOD	V. FINE	UNC.
☐ 1902	Lyon-Roberts	Red	55.00	100.00	225.00	1000.00
☐ 1902	Lyons-Treat	Red	55.00	55.00	225.00	1000.00
☐ 1902	Vernon-Treat	Red	55.00	55.00	225.00	1200.00

Second Issue—
Date 1902-1908 added on back, Treasury seal and serial numbers blue.

☐ 1902	Lyons-Roberts	Blue	30.00	50.00	75.00	385.00
☐ 1902	Lyons-Treat	Blue	30.00	50.00	75.00	385.00
☐ 1902	Vernon-Treat	Blue	30.00	50.00	75.00	385.00
☐ 1902	Vernon-McClung	Blue	30.00	50.00	75.00	385.00
☐ 1902	Napier-McClung	Blue	30.00	50.00	75.00	385.00
☐ 1902	Napier-Thompson	Blue	30.00	50.00	90.00	385.00
☐ 1902	Napier-Burke	Blue	30.00	50.00	75.00	385.00
☐ 1902	Parker-Burke	Blue	30.00	50.00	75.00	385.00

Third Issue—
Date 1902-1908 removed from back, seal and serial numbers are blue.

☐ 1902	Lyons-Roberts	Blue	27.50	45.00	65.00	350.00
☐ 1902	Lyons-Treat	Blue	27.50	45.00	65.00	350.00
☐ 1902	Vernon-Treat	Blue	27.50	45.00	65.00	350.00
☐ 1902	Vernon-McClung	Blue	27.50	45.00	65.00	350.00
☐ 1902	Napier-McClung	Blue	27.50	45.00	65.00	350.00
☐ 1902	Napier-Thompson	Blue	27.50	45.00	65.00	350.00
☐ 1902	Napier-Burke	Blue	27.50	45.00	65.00	350.00
☐ 1902	Parker-Burke	Blue	27.50	45.00	65.00	350.00
☐ 1902	Teehee-Burke	Blue	27.50	45.00	65.00	350.00
☐ 1902	Elliott-Burke	Blue	27.50	45.00	65.00	350.00
☐ 1902	Elliott-White	Blue	27.50	45.00	65.00	350.00
☐ 1902	Speelman-White	Blue	27.50	45.00	65.00	350.00
☐ 1902	Woods-White	Blue	27.50	45.00	125.00	425.00
☐ 1902	Woods-Tate	Blue	40.00	75.00	200.00	550.00
☐ 1902	Jones-Woods	Blue	100.00	200.00	500.00	2750.00

Face Design: TYPE I Portrait of President Jackson in center, name of Bank to left, brown seal right. Charter number in black.

Face Design: TYPE II

Back Design: The White House, similar to all $20.00 small Notes.

SERIES	SIGNATURES	SEAL	A.B.P.	GOOD	V. FINE	UNC.
☐ 1929—TYPE I	Jones-Woods	Brown	22.00	27.50	35.00	85.00
☐ 1929—TYPE II	Jones-Woods	Brown	22.00	32.50	40.00	100.00

Face Design: Portrait of Stephen Decatur left. "TWENTY SILVER DOLLARS", in center.

Back Design: "SILVER" in large block letters.

SERIES	SIGNATURES	SEAL	A.B.P.	GOOD	V. FINE	UNC.
☐ 1880	Scofield-Gilfillan	Brown	150.00	300.00	1000.00	8200.00
☐ 1880	Bruce-Gilfillan	Brown	150.00	300.00	1000.00	8200.00
☐ 1880	Bruce-Wyman	Brown	150.00	300.00	1000.00	8200.00
☐ 1880	Bruce-Wyman	Red Sm.	150.00	300.00	2750.00	8500.00

This Note was also issued in series of 1878. They are very rare.

$20.00

Face Design: Portrait of Daniel Manning center, Agriculture left, Industry right.

Back Design: Double diamond design center.

SERIES	SIGNATURES	SEAL	A.B.P.	GOOD	V. FINE	UNC.
☐ 1886	Rosecrans-Hyatt	Red Lg	125.00	250.00	2000.00	8750.00
☐ 1886	Rosecrans-Huston	Brown Lg	125.00	250.00	2000.00	9000.00
☐ 1886	Rosecrans-Nebeker	Brown Lg	125.00	250.00	2000.00	9000.00
☐ 1886	Rosecrans-Nebeker	Red Sm	125.00	300.00	2500.00	9250.00

TWENTY DOLLAR NOTES (1891) SILVER CERTIFICATES
(NOT ISSUED IN SMALL SIZE NOTES)

(Large Size)

Face Design: Same as Note No. 92.

Back Design: Revised.

SERIES	SIGNATURES	SEAL	A.B.P.	GOOD	V. FINE	UNC.
☐1891	Rosecrans-Nebeker	Red	52.50	100.00	325.00	1500.00
☐1891	Tillman-Morgan	Red	52.50	100.00	325.00	1500.00
☐1891	Bruce-Roberts	Red	52.50	100.00	325.00	1500.00
☐1891	Lyons-Roberts	Red	52.50	100.00	325.00	1500.00
☐1891	Parker-Burke	Blue	52.50	100.00	300.00	3750.00
☐1891	Teehee-Burke	Blue	52.50	100.00	300.00	3750.00

TWENTY DOLLAR NOTES (1882) GOLD CERTIFICATES

(Large Size)

Face Design: Portrait of President Garfield right, "TWENTY DOLLARS IN GOLD COIN" center.

Back Design: Large "20" left, Eagle and arrows center, bright orange color.

SERIES	SIGNATURES	SEAL	A.B.P.	GOOD	V. FINE	UNC.
☐1882	Bruce-Gilfillan	Brown	200.00	500.00	2000.00	12000.00
The above Note has a countersigned signature.						
☐1882	Bruce-Gilfillan	Brown	60.00	150.00	850.00	8500.00
☐1882	Bruce-Wyman	Brown	60.00	150.00	850.00	8500.00
☐1882	Rosecrans-Huston	Brown	60.00	150.00	850.00	8500.00
☐1882	Lyons-Roberts	Red	50.00	100.00	350.00	2750.00

Face Design: Portrait of President Washingtoncenter, "XX"left,
Treasury Sealleft.

Back Design: Eagle and Shieldcenter, printed in bright orange color.

SERIES	SIGNATURES	SEAL	A.B.P.	GOOD	V. FINE	UNC.
☐1905	Lyons-Roberts	Red	100.00	200.00	1500.00	11500.00
☐1905	Lyons-Treat	Red	100.00	200.00	1500.00	11500.00
☐1906	Vernon-Treat	Gold	30.00	45.00	90.00	850.00
☐1906	Vernon-McClung	Gold	30.00	45.00	90.00	850.00
☐1906	Napier-McClung	Gold	30.00	45.00	90.00	850.00
☐1906	Napier-Thompson	Gold	30.00	50.00	100.00	850.00
☐1906	Parker-Burke	Gold	30.00	42.50	85.00	850.00
☐1906	Teehee-Burke	Gold	30.00	42.50	85.00	850.00
☐1922	Speelman-White	Gold	25.00	40.00	75.00	725.00

$20.00

Face Design: Portrait of President Jackson center, gold seal left, gold serial numbers.

Back Design: The White House, printed green, similar to all small size $20's.

SERIES	SIGNATURES	SEAL	A.B.P.	V. FINE	UNC.
☐ 1928	Woods-Mellon	Gold	25.00	45.00	200.00

TWENTY DOLLAR NOTES (1890) TREASURY NOTES

(Large Size)

Face Design: Portrait of John Marshall, Chief Justice Supreme Court left, "20" center.

Back Design

SERIES	SIGNATURES	SEAL	A.B.P.	GOOD	V. FINE	UNC.
☐ 1890	Rosecrans-Huston	Brown	200.00	475.00	2500.00	12000.00
☐ 1890	Rosecrans-Nebeker	Brown	200.00	475.00	2500.00	12000.00
☐ 1890	Rosecrans-Nebeker	Red	200.00	475.00	2500.00	12000.00

(Large Size)

Back Design

Face Design: Same as previous Note.

SERIES	SIGNATURES	SEAL	A.B.P.	GOOD	V. FINE	UNC.
☐ 1891	Tillman-Morgan	Red	300.00	800.00	3500.00	13500.00
☐ 1891	Bruce-Roberts	Red	300.00	675.00	3500.00	15000.00

$20.00

Face Design: Portrait of President Cleveland center, Federal Reserve Seal left, Treasury Seal right.

Back Design: Scenes of transportation. Locomotive left, Steamship right.

SERIES OF 1914 — SIGNATURES OF BURKE-McADOO, RED TREASURY SEAL

BANK	A.B.P.	V.FINE	UNC.	BANK	A.B.P.	V.FINE	UNC.
☐ Boston	40.00	135.00	800.00	☐ Chicago	40.00	135.00	800.00
☐ New York	40.00	135.00	800.00	☐ St. Louis	40.00	135.00	800.00
☐ Philadelphia	40.00	135.00	800.00	☐ Minneapolis	40.00	135.00	800.00
☐ Cleveland	40.00	135.00	800.00	☐ Kansas City	40.00	135.00	800.00
☐ Richmond	40.00	135.00	800.00	☐ Dallas	40.00	135.00	800.00
☐ Atlanta	40.00	135.00	800.00	☐ San Francisco	40.00	135.00	800.00

SERIES OF 1914 — WITH BLUE TREASURY SEAL AND BLUE SERIAL NUMBERS

This Note was issued with signatures of BURKE-McADOO, BURKE-GLASS, BURKE-HUSTON and WHITE-MELLON.

	A.B.P.	V.FINE	UNC.
Issued to all Federal Reserve Banks	27.50	52.50	235.00

Face Design: Portrait of President Jackson center, black Federal Reserve Seal with numeral for district in center. City of issuing bank in seal circle. Green Treasury Seal right.

Back Design: Picture of the White House, similar to all small size $20.00 notes.

$20.00

SERIES OF 1928 — SIGNATURES OF TATE-MELLON, GREEN SEAL

BANK	A.B.P.	V.FINE	UNC.	BANK	A.B.P.	V.FINE	UNC.
Boston	22.50	30.00	65.00	Chicago	22.50	30.00	55.00
New York	22.50	30.00	60.00	St. Louis	22.50	35.00	75.00
Philadelphia	22.50	30.00	65.00	Minneapolis	22.50	40.00	80.00
Cleveland	22.50	30.00	65.00	Kansas City	22.50	35.00	80.00
Richmond	22.50	40.00	75.00	Dallas	22.50	35.00	80.00
Atlanta	22.50	35.00	65.00	San Francisco	22.50	30.00	75.00

SERIES OF 1928A — SIGNATURES OF WOODS-MELLON, GREEN SEAL

CITY	A.B.P.	V.FINE	UNC.	CITY	A.B.P.	V.FINE	UNC.
Boston	24.00	45.00	65.00	Chicago	24.00	45.00	70.00
New York	24.00	50.00	75.00	St. Louis	24.00	50.00	75.00
Philadelphia	24.00	45.00	65.00	Minneapolis		NOT ISSUED	
Cleveland	24.00	50.00	70.00	Kansas City	24.00	60.00	100.00
Richmond	24.00	50.00	75.00	Dallas	24.00	40.00	80.00
Atlanta	24.00	50.00	70.00	San Francisco		NOT ISSUED	

TWENTY DOLLAR NOTES (1928) FEDERAL RESERVE NOTES
(Small Size)

NOTE NO. 100

SERIES OF 1928B — SIGNATURES OF WOODS-MELLON, GREEN SEAL
FACE AND BACK DESIGN SIMILAR TO PREVIOUS NOTE. NUMERAL IN
FEDERAL RESERVE SEAL IS NOW CHANGED TO A LETTER.

BANK	A.B.P.	V.FINE	UNC.	BANK	A.B.P.	V.FINE	UNC.
☐Boston	22.50	37.50	55.00	☐Chicago	22.50	37.50	55.00
☐New York	22.50	37.50	55.00	☐St. Louis	22.50	37.50	65.00
☐Philadelphia	22.50	37.50	55.00	☐Minneapolis	22.50	37.50	60.00
☐Cleveland	22.50	37.50	55.00	☐Kansas City	22.50	37.50	60.00
☐Richmond	22.50	37.50	55.00	☐Dallas	22.50	37.50	70.00
☐Atlanta	22.50	37.50	60.00	☐San Francisco	22.50	37.50	60.00

SERIES OF 1928C — SIGNATURES OF WOODS-MILLS, GREEN SEAL
ONLY TWO BANKS ISSUED THIS NOTE.

BANK	A.B.P.	V.FINE	UNC.	BANK	A.B.P.	V.FINE	UNC.
☐Chicago	25.00	50.00	125.00	☐San Francisco	25.00	50.00	140.00

TWENTY DOLLAR NOTES (1934) FEDERAL RESERVE NOTES
(Small Size)

NOTE NO. 100A

FACE AND BACK DESIGN SIMILAR TO PREVIOUS NOTE. "REDEEMABLE
IN GOLD" REMOVED FROM OBLIGATION OVER FEDERAL RESERVE
SEAL. SIGNATURES OF JULIAN-MORGENTHAU, GREEN SEAL.

BANK	GOOD	V.FINE	UNC.	BANK	GOOD	V.FINE	UNC.
☐Boston	——	35.00	55.00	☐St. Louis	——	35.00	50.00
☐New York	——	35.00	50.00	☐Minneapolis	——	35.00	50.00
☐Philadelphia	——	35.00	50.00	☐Kansas City	——	35.00	50.00
☐Cleveland	——	35.00	50.00	☐Dallas	——	35.00	50.00
☐Richmond	——	35.00	50.00	☐San Francisco	——	35.00	50.00
☐Atlanta	——	35.00	50.00	☐*San Francisco			
☐Chicago	——	35.00	50.00	(HAWAII)	50.00	165.00	850.00

*The San Francisco Federal Reserve Note with brown seal and brown
serial numbers, and overprinted "HAWAII" on face and back, was a special
issue for the Armed Forces in the Pacific area during World War II.

SERIES OF 1934A — SIGNATURES OF JULIAN-MORGENTHAU

BANK	V.FINE	UNC.	BANK	V.FINE	UNC.
☐ Boston	30.00	50.00	☐ St. Louis	30.00	55.00
☐ New York	30.00	50.00	☐ Minneapolis	30.00	60.00
☐ Philadelphia	30.00	50.00	☐ Kansas City	30.00	55.00
☐ Cleveland	30.00	50.00	☐ Dallas	30.00	50.00
☐ Richmond	30.00	50.00	☐ San Francisco	30.00	50.00
☐ Atlanta	30.00	50.00	☐ *San Francisco (HAWAII)	40.00	125.00
☐ Chicago	30.00	55.00			

SERIES OF 1934B — SIGNATURES OF JULIAN-VINSON, GREEN SEAL

BANK	V.FINE	UNC.	BANK	V.FINE	UNC.
☐ Boston	30.00	55.00	☐ Chicago	30.00	45.00
☐ New York	30.00	50.00	☐ St. Louis	30.00	50.00
☐ Philadelphia	30.00	50.00	☐ Minneapolis	30.00	55.00
☐ Cleveland	30.00	55.00	☐ Kansas City	30.00	50.00
☐ Richmond	30.00	50.00	☐ Dallas	32.50	55.00
☐ Atlanta	30.00	45.00	☐ San Francisco	30.00	50.00

SERIES OF 1934C — SIGNATURES OF JULIAN-SNYDER, GREEN SEAL

Back Design: Back has been modified with this series, balcony added to the White House.

BANK	V.FINE	UNC.	BANK	V.FINE	UNC.
☐ Boston	30.00	55.00	☐ Chicago	30.00	50.00
☐ New York	30.00	50.00	☐ St. Louis	30.00	50.00
☐ Philadelphia	30.00	50.00	☐ Minneapolis	30.00	60.00
☐ Cleveland	30.00	50.00	☐ Kansas City	30.00	55.00
☐ Richmond	30.00	50.00	☐ Dallas	30.00	55.00
☐ Atlanta	30.00	50.00	☐ San Francisco	30.00	50.00

SERIES OF 1934D — SIGNATURES OF CLARK-SNYDER, GREEN SEAL

BANK	V.FINE	UNC.	BANK	V.FINE	UNC.
☐ Boston	30.00	50.00	☐ Chicago	30.00	50.00
☐ New York	30.00	50.00	☐ St. Louis	30.00	50.00
☐ Philadelphia	30.00	50.00	☐ Minneapolis	30.00	55.00
☐ Cleveland	30.00	50.00	☐ Kansas City	30.00	55.00
☐ Richmond	30.00	50.00	☐ Dallas	30.00	52.50
☐ Atlanta	30.00	50.00	☐ San Francisco	30.00	52.50

$20.00

TWENTY DOLLAR NOTES (1950) FEDERAL RESERVE NOTES

(Small Size)   NOTE NO. 102

SERIES OF 1950 — SIGNATURES OF CLARK-SNYDER

Black Federal Reserve Seal and Green Treasury Seal are slightly smaller.

BANK	UNC.	BANK	UNC.
☐ Boston	40.00	☐ Chicago	40.00
☐ New York	40.00	☐ St. Louis	40.00
☐ Philadelphia	40.00	☐ Minneapolis	48.00
☐ Cleveland	40.00	☐ Kansas City	45.00
☐ Richmond	40.00	☐ Dallas	45.00
☐ Atlanta	40.00	☐ San Francisco	40.00

SERIES OF 1950A — SIGNATURES OF PRIEST-HUMPHREY, GREEN SEAL
Issued for all Federal Reserve Banks..32.50

SERIES OF 1950B — SIGNATURES OF PRIEST-ANDERSON, GREEN SEAL
Issued for all Federal Reserve Banks..32.50

SERIES OF 1950C — SIGNATURES OF SMITH-DILLON, GREEN SEAL
Issued for all Federal ReserveBanks...32.00

SERIES OF 1950D — SIGNATURES OF GRANAHAN-DILLON, GREEN SEAL
Issued for all Federal Reserve Banks..32.00

SERIES OF 1950E — SIGNATURES OF GRANAHAN-FOWLER, GREEN SEAL
Issued only for New York, Chicago and San Francisco..........................35.00

TWENTY DOLLAR NOTES (1963) FEDERAL RESERVE NOTES

(Small Size)   NOTE NO. 102A

SERIES OF 1963 — SIGNATURES OF GRANAHAN-DILLON, GREEN SEAL
Issued for all Federal Reserve Banks except Philadelphia and Minneapolis..........30.00

SERIES OF 1963A—SIGNATURES OF GRANAHAN-FOWLER, GREEN SEAL
Issued for all Federal Reserve Bank...29.00

SERIES OF 1969 — SIGNATURES OF ELSTON-KENNEDY, GREEN SEAL
Issued for all Federal Reserve Banks..26.00

SERIES OF 1969A — SIGNATURES OF KABIS-CONNALLY, GREEN SEAL
Issued for all Federal Reserve Banks..24.00

SERIES OF 1969B — SIGNATURES OF BANUELOS-CONNALLY, GREEN SEAL
Issued for all Federal Reserve Banks..24.00

SERIES OF 1969C — SIGNATURES OF BANUELOS-SHULTZ, GREEN SEAL
Issued for all Federal Reserve Banks..24.00

SERIES OF 1974 — SIGNATURES OF NEFF-SIMON, GREEN SEAL
Issued for all Federal Reserve Banks..22.00

SERIES OF 1977 — SIGNATURES OF MORTON-BLUMENTHAL, GREEN SEAL
Issued for all Federal Reserve Banks..22.00

SERIES OF 1977A — SIGNATURES OF MORTON-MILLER, GREEN SEAL
Issued for all Federal Reserve Banks..CURRENT

TWENTY DOLLAR NOTES (1915) FEDERAL RESERVE BANK
(ALL HAVE BLUE SEALS)

(Large Size)

NOTE NO. 103

Face Design: Portrait of President Cleveland left, name of Bank and city center, blue Seal right.

Back Design: Locomotive and Steamship, same as Page 124, similar to Note No. 98.

$20.00

BANK & CITY	SERIES	GOV'T SIGNATURES	BANK SIGNATURES	A.B.P.	GOOD	V. FINE	UNC.
☐Atlanta	1915	Teehee-Burke	Bell-Wellborn	60.00	100.00	430.00	2750.00
☐Atlanta	1918	Elliott-Burke	Bell-Wellborn	60.00	100.00	475.00	2875.00
☐Chicago	1915	Teehee-Burke	McLallen-McDougal	60.00	100.00	425.00	2750.00
☐St. Louis	1915	Teehee-Burke	Attebery-Wells ..	100.00	185.00	475.00	2875.00
☐Kan. City	1915	Teehee-Burke	Anderson-Miller ..	60.00	100.00	425.00	2750.00
☐Kan. City	1915	Teehee-Burke	Cross-Miller	60.00	100.00	425.00	2750.00
☐Dallas	1915	Teehee-Burke	Hoopes-VanZandt .	75.00	150.00	425.00	2750.00
☐Dallas	1915	Teehee-Burke	Gilbert-VanZandt	100.00	200.00	425.00	2750.00
☐Dallas	1915	Teehee-Burke	Talley-VanZandt ..	75.00	150.00	425.00	2750.00

TWENTY DOLLAR NOTES (1929) FEDERAL RESERVE BANK NOTES
(Small Size)

NOTE NO. 103A

Face Design: Portrait of President Jackson center, name of bank left, brown seal right. Brown serial number, district letter in black. Signatures of Jones-Woods.

Back Design: The White House.

BANK	A.B.P.	V.FINE	UNC.	BANK	A.B.P.	V.FINE	UNC.
☐Boston	22.00	40.00	80.00	☐Chicago	22.00	40.00	65.00
☐New York	22.00	40.00	70.00	☐St. Louis	25.00	40.00	90.00
☐Philadelphia ...	22.00	40.00	70.00	☐Minneapolis ...	25.00	40.00	75.00
☐Cleveland	22.00	40.00	70.00	☐Kansas City	25.00	40.00	80.00
☐Richmond	22.00	40.00	70.00	☐Dallas	25.00	40.00	110.00
☐Atlanta	25.00	40.00	75.00	☐San Francisco ..	25.00	40.00	100.00

FIFTY DOLLAR NOTES

ORDER OF ISSUE

FIFTY DOLLAR NOTES (1862-1863) UNITED STATES NOTES
(ALSO KNOWN AS LEGAL TENDER NOTES)

(Large Size)

Face Design: Portrait of Hamilton to left.

$50.00

Back Design

SERIES	SIGNATURES	SEAL	A.B.P.	GOOD	V. FINE	UNC.
☐ 1862	Chittenden-Spinner*	Red	400.00	700.00	3500.00	13000.00
☐ 1862	Chittenden-Spinner**	Red	400.00	700.00	3500.00	13000.00
☐ 1863	Chittenden-Spinner**	Red	400.00	700.00	3500.00	13000.00

*First Obligation: Similar to Note No. 33   **Second Obligation: Shown above.

FIFTY DOLLAR NOTES (1869) UNITED STATES NOTES
(ALSO KNOWN AS LEGAL TENDER NOTE)

(Large Size)

Face Design: Portrait of Henry Clay to right.

Back Design

SERIES	SIGNATURES	SEAL	A.B.P.	GOOD	V. FINE	UNC.
☐1869	Allison-Spinner	Red	1250.00	3500.00	7500.00	25000.00

NOTE: Only 24 pieces of this Note remain unredeemed.

Face Design: Franklin to left.

Back Design

$50.00

SERIES	SIGNATURES	SEAL	A.B.P.	GOOD	V. FINE	UNC.
☐ 1874	Allison-Spinner	Sm. Red	185.00	500.00	2250.00	12000.00
☐ 1875	Allison-Wyman	Sm. Red	135.00	350.00	1850.00	10000.00
☐ 1878	Allison-Gilfillan	Sm. Red	135.00	350.00	1875.00	8750.00
☐ 1880	Bruce-Gilfillan	Lg. Brown	110.00	215.00	700.00	4000.00
☐ 1880	Bruce-Wyman	Lg. Brown	110.00	215.00	700.00	4000.00
☐ 1880	Rosecrans-Jordan	Lg. Red	110.00	215.00	700.00	3250.00
☐ 1880	Rosecrans-Hyatt	Lg. Red	110.00	215.00	700.00	3250.00
☐ 1880	Rosecrans-Hyatt	Lg. Red	110.00	215.00	700.00	3250.00
☐ 1880	Rosecrans-Huston	Lg. Red	110.00	215.00	700.00	3250.00
☐ 1880	Rosecrans-Huston	Lg. Brown	110.00	215.00	700.00	2750.00
☐ 1880	Tillman-Morgan	Sm. Red	100.00	185.00	700.00	2600.00
☐ 1880	Bruce-Roberts	Sm. Red	100.00	185.00	700.00	2600.00
☐ 1880	Lyons-Roberts	Sm. Red	100.00	185.00	700.00	2600.00

Face Design: Washington crossing Delaware left, Washington at Valley Forge, right.

Back Design: Embarkation of the Pilgrims.

SERIES	SIGNATURES	SEAL	A.B.P.	V. FINE	UNC.
☐Original	Chittenden-Spinner	Red/rays	315.00	1000.00	3850.00
☐Original	Colby-Spinner	Red/rays	315.00	1000.00	3850.00
☐Original	Allison-Spinner	Red/rays	315.00	1000.00	3850.00
☐1875	Allison-New	Red/Scals.	300.00	975.00	3700.00
☐1875	Allison-Wyman	Red/Scals.	300.00	975.00	3700.00
☐1875	Allison-Gilfillan	Red/Scals.	300.00	975.00	3700.00
☐1875	Scofield-Gilfillan	Red/Scals.	300.00	975.00	3700.00
☐1875	Bruce-Gilfillan	Red/Scals.	300.00	975.00	3700.00
☐1875	Bruce-Wyman	Red/Scals.	300.00	975.00	3700.00
☐1875	Rosecrans-Huston	Red/Scals.	300.00	975.00	3700.00
☐1875	Rosecrans-Nebeker	Red/Scals.	300.00	975.00	3700.00
☐1875	Tillman-Morgan	Red/Scals.	300.00	975.00	3700.00

First Issue—brown seal and brown backs.

Back Design of Note No. 108
Face Design: Similar to Note No. 107

$50.00

SERIES	SIGNATURES	SEAL	A.B.P.	GOOD	V. FINE	UNC.
☐1882	Bruce-Gilfillan	Brown	100.00	175.00	500.00	2250.00
☐1882	Bruce-Wyman	Brown	100.00	175.00	500.00	2250.00
☐1882	Bruce-Jordan	Brown	100.00	175.00	500.00	2250.00
☐1882	Rosecrans-Jordan	Brown	100.00	175.00	500.00	2250.00
☐1882	Rosecrans-Hyatt	Brown	100.00	175.00	500.00	2250.00
☐1882	Rosecrans-Huston	Brown	100.00	175.00	500.00	2250.00
☐1882	Rosecrans-Nebeker	Brown	100.00	175.00	500.00	2250.00
☐1882	Rosecrans-Morgan	Brown	150.00	400.00	1350.00	3500.00
☐1882	Tillman-Morgan	Brown	100.00	175.00	500.00	2250.00
☐1882	Tillman-Roberts	Brown	100.00	175.00	500.00	2250.00
☐1882	Bruce-Roberts	Brown	100.00	175.00	500.00	2250.00
☐1882	Lyons-Roberts	Brown	100.00	175.00	500.00	2250.00
☐1882	Vernon-Treat	Brown	150.00	400.00	1350.00	3500.00

FIFTY DOLLAR NOTES (1882) NATIONAL BANK NOTES
SECOND CHARTER PERIOD (Large Size)
NOTE NO. 108A

Second Issue—blue seal, green back with date 1902-1908

Face Design: Washington crossing Delaware left, Washington at Valley Forge, right.

Back Design

SERIES	SIGNATURES	SEAL	A.B.P.	GOOD	V. FINE	UNC.
☐ 1882	Rosecrans-Huston	Blue	100.00	160.00	450.00	2875.00
☐ 1882	Rosecrans-Nebeker	Blue	100.00	160.00	450.00	2875.00
☐ 1882	Tillman-Morgan	Blue	100.00	160.00	450.00	2875.00
☐ 1882	Tillman-Roberts	Blue	100.00	160.00	450.00	2875.00
☐ 1882	Bruce-Roberts	Blue	100.00	160.00	450.00	2875.00
☐ 1882	Lyons-Roberts	Blue	100.00	160.00	450.00	2875.00
☐ 1882	Vernon-Treat	Blue	100.00	160.00	450.00	2875.00
☐ 1882	Napier-McClung	Blue	100.00	275.00	525.00	3300.00

First Issues — red seal and numbers.

Face Design: Portrait of Sherman left. Name of Bank Center.
Treasury Seal and numbers.

$50.00

SERIES	SIGNATURES	SEAL	A.B.P.	GOOD	V. FINE	UNC.
☐1902	Lyons-Roberts	Red	100.00	225.00	850.00	5000.00
☐1902	Lyons-Treat	Red	100.00	225.00	850.00	5000.00
☐1902	Vernon-Treat	Red	100.00	225.00	850.00	5000.00

Second Issue — Treasury Seal
and numbers remain blue, date 1902-1908 added on back.

☐1902	Lyons-Roberts	Blue	62.50	85.00	265.00	725.00
☐1902	Lyons-Treat	Blue	62.50	85.00	265.00	725.00
☐1902	Vernon-Treat	Blue	62.50	85.00	265.00	725.00
☐1902	Vernon-McClung	Blue	62.50	85.00	265.00	725.00
☐1902	Napier-McClung	Blue	62.50	85.00	265.00	725.00
☐1902	Napier-Thompson	Blue	62.50	85.00	265.00	725.00
☐1902	Napier-Burke	Blue	62.50	85.00	265.00	725.00
☐1902	Parker-Burke	Blue	62.50	85.00	265.00	725.00
☐1902	Teehee-Burke	Blue	75.00	125.00	350.00	725.00

Third Issue — Treasury Seal
and numbers remain blue, date of 1902-1908 removed from back.

☐1902	Lyons-Roberts	Blue	67.50	100.00	250.00	675.00
☐1902	Lyons-Treat	Blue	67.50	100.00	250.00	675.00
☐1902	Vernon-Treat	Blue	67.50	100.00	250.00	675.00
☐1902	Vernon-McClung	Blue	67.50	100.00	250.00	675.00
☐1902	Napier-McClung	Blue	67.50	100.00	250.00	675.00
☐1902	Napier-Thompson	Blue	67.50	100.00	250.00	675.00
☐1902	Napier-Burke	Blue	67.50	100.00	250.00	675.00
☐1902	Parker-Burke	Blue	67.50	100.00	250.00	675.00
☐1902	Teehee-Burke	Blue	67.50	100.00	250.00	675.00
☐1902	Elliott-Burke	Blue	67.50	100.00	250.00	675.00
☐1902	Elliott-White	Blue	67.50	100.00	250.00	675.00
☐1875	Speelman-White	Blue	67.50	100.00	250.00	675.00
☐1902	Woods-White	Blue	67.50	100.00	250.00	675.00

Face Design: Portrait of President Grant center. Bank left. brown seal right. Brown serial numbers, black Charter numbers.

Back Design: The Capitol.

SERIES	SIGNATURES	SEAL	A.B.P.	V. FINE	UNC.
☐ 1929 TYPE I*	Jones-Wood	Brown	55.00	100.00	165.00
☐ 1929 TYPE II*	Jones-Wood	Brown	57.50	160.00	260.00

*See Page 63. TYPE I—Charter number in black.
TYPE II—Similar. Charter number added in brown.

Face Design: Portrait of Edward Everett.

Back Design

SERIES	SIGNATURES	SEAL	A.B.P.	GOOD	V. FINE
☐1878	Varied	Red		VERY RARE	
☐1880	Scofield-Gilfillan	Brown	1100.00	2500.00	6000.00
☐1880	Bruce-Gilfillan	Brown	1000.00	2500.00	6000.00
☐1880	Bruce-Wyman	Brown	1000.00	2500.00	6000.00
☐1880	Rosecrans-Huston	Brown	1000.00	2500.00	6000.00
☐1880	Rosecrans-Nebeker	Red	1000.00	2500.00	6000.00

$50.00

Face Design: Portrait of Edward Everett.

Back Design

SERIES	SIGNATURES	SEAL	A.B.P.	GOOD	V. FINE	UNC.
1891	Rosecrans-Nebeker	Red	135.00	225.00	750.00	6700.00
1891	Tillman-Morgan	Red	135.00	225.00	750.00	6700.00
1891	Bruce-Roberts	Red	135.00	225.00	750.00	6700.00
1891	Lyons-Roberts	Red	135.00	225.00	750.00	6700.00
1891	Vernon-Treat	Red	135.00	225.00	750.00	6700.00
1891	Parker-Burke	Blue	135.00	225.00	750.00	6200.00

Face Design: Portrait of Silas Wright to left.

$50.00

Back Design: Bright yellow color.

SERIES	SIGNATURES	SEAL	A.B.P.	GOOD	V. FINE	UNC.
☐1882	Bruce-Gilfillan	Brown	300.00	1000.00	3500.00	22500.00
☐1882	Bruce-Wyman	Brown	100.00	220.00	1600.00	15000.00
☐1882	Rosecrans-Hyatt	Red	100.00	220.00	1600.00	15000.00
☐1882	Rosecrans-Huston	Brown	100.00	220.00	1600.00	15000.00
☐1882	Lyons-Roberts	Red	90.00	180.00	550.00	4200.00
☐1882	Lyons-Treat	Red	90.00	180.00	550.00	4200.00
☐1882	Vernon-Treat	Red	90.00	180.00	550.00	4200.00
☐1882	Vernon-McClung	Red	90.00	180.00	550.00	4200.00
☐1882	Napier-McClung	Red	90.00	180.00	550.00	4200.00

FIFTY DOLLAR NOTES (1913) GOLD CERTIFICATES
(Large Size)

Face Design: Portrait of President Grant.

Back Design: Bright yellow color.

SERIES	SIGNATURES	SEAL	A.B.P.	GOOD	V. FINE	UNC.
☐ 1913	Parker-Burke	Gold	75.00	110.00	365.00	2750.00
☐ 1913	Teehee-Burke	Gold	75.00	110.00	365.00	2750.00
☐ 1922	Speelman-White	Gold	75.00	110.00	300.00	1750.00

FIFTY DOLLAR NOTES (1928) GOLD CERTIFICATES
(Small Size)

Back Design: Same as Note No. 110.

SERIES	SIGNATURES	SEAL	A.B.P.	GOOD	V. FINE	UNC.
☐ 1928	Woods-Mellon	Gold	53.50	70.00	120.00	450.00

FIFTY DOLLAR NOTES (1891) TREASURY NOTES
(Large Size)

Face Design: Portrait of William H. Seward. Only 25 pieces remain unredeemed.

Back Design: Green.

SERIES	SIGNATURES	SEAL	A.B.P.	GOOD	V. FINE	UNC.
☐ 1891	Rosecrans-Nebeker	Red	1250.00	4500.00	15000.00	RARE

FIFTY DOLLAR NOTES (1914) FEDERAL RESERVE NOTES

(Large Size)

SERIES OF 1914 — SIGNATURES OF BURKE-McADOO
RED SEAL AND RED SERIAL NUMBERS

CITY	A.B.P.	GOOD	V.FINE	UNC.	CITY	A.B.P.	GOOD	V.FINE	UNC.
☐ Boston	65.00	100.00	300.00	2000.00	☐ Chicago	65.00	100.00	300.00	2000.00
☐ New York	65.00	100.00	300.00	2000.00	☐ St. Louis	65.00	100.00	300.00	2000.00
☐ Philadelphia	65.00	100.00	300.00	2000.00	☐ Minneapolis	65.00	100.00	300.00	2000.00
☐ Cleveland	65.00	100.00	300.00	2000.00	☐ Kansas City	65.00	100.00	300.00	2000.00
☐ Richmond	65.00	100.00	300.00	2000.00	☐ Dallas	65.00	100.00	300.00	2000.00
☐ Atlanta	65.00	100.00	300.00	2000.00	☐ San Fran.	65.00	100.00	300.00	2000.00

SERIES OF 1914—DESIGN CONTINUES AS PREVIOUS NOTE.
THE SEAL AND SERIAL NUMBERS ARE NOW BLUE.

*(This Note was issued with various signatures for each Bank.)

BANK	A.B.P.	GOOD	V.FINE	UNC.	BANK	A.B.P.	GOOD	V.FINE	UNC.
☐ Boston	55.00	80.00	125.00	650.00	☐ Chicago	55.00	80.00	125.00	650.00
☐ New York	55.00	80.00	125.00	650.00	☐ St. Louis	55.00	80.00	125.00	650.00
☐ Philadelphia	55.00	80.00	125.00	650.00	☐ Minneapolis	55.00	80.00	125.00	650.00
☐ Cleveland	55.00	80.00	125.00	650.00	☐ Kansas City	55.00	80.00	125.00	650.00
☐ Richmond	55.00	80.00	125.00	650.00	☐ Dallas	55.00	80.00	125.00	650.00
☐ Atlanta	55.00	80.00	125.00	650.00	☐ San Fran.	55.00	80.00	125.00	650.00

*Signatures: Burke-McAdoo, Burke-Glass, Burke-Huston, White-Mellon.

FIFTY DOLLAR (1928-1934) FEDERAL RESERVE NOTES
(Small Size)   **NOTE NO. 116**

Face Design: Portrait of President Grant center, Black Federal
Reserve Seal with number to left. Green Treasury Seal to right.

Back Design: Same as Note No. 110.
SERIES OF 1928 — SIGNATURES OF WOODS-MELLON, GREEN SEAL

	A.B.P.	V.FINE	UNC.
Issued for all Federal Reserve Banks	52.00	75.00	135.00

(Small Size)   **NOTE NO. 116A**
SERIES OF 1928A — SIGNATURES OF WOODS-MELLON, GREEN SEAL
   LETTER REPLACES NUMERAL IN FEDERAL RESERVE SEAL

Issued for all Federal Reserve Banks	52.00	72.00	110.00

(Small Size)   **NOTE NO. 116B**
SERIES OF 1934—SIGNATURES OF JULIAN-MORGENTHAU, GREEN SEAL

Issued for all Federal Reserve Banks	——	65.00	95.00

SERIES OF 1934A—SIGNATURES OF JULIAN-MORGENTHAU, GREEN SEAL
Issued for all Federal Reserve Banks except

Philadelphia	——	70.00	100.00

SERIES OF 1934B — SIGNATURES OF JULIAN-VINSON, GREEN SEAL
Issued for all Federal Reserve Banks except

Boston and New York	——	75.00	120.00

SERIES OF 1934C — SIGNATURES OF JULIAN-SNYDER, GREEN SEAL
Issued for all Federal Reserve Banks except San

Francisco	——	67.50	95.00

SERIES OF 1934D — SIGNATURES OF CLARK-SNYDER, GREEN SEAL
Issued for Cleveland, St. Louis,Minneapolis,

Kansas City, San Francisco	——	65.00	90.00

$50.00

FIFTY DOLLAR NOTES (1950) FEDERAL RESERVE NOTES

(Small Size)   NOTE NO. 116C

SERIES OF 1950 — SIGNATURES OF CLARK-SNYDER
FEDERAL RESERVE AND TREASURY SEALS ARE NOW SMALLER

	UNC.
Issued for all Federal Reserve Banks	80.00

SERIES OF 1950A — SIGNATURES OF PRIEST-HUMPHREY
Issued for all Federal Reserve Banks except Minneapolis 80.00

SERIES OF 1950B — SIGNATURES OF PRIEST-ANDERSON
Issued for all Federal Reserve Banks except Atlanta and Minneapolis 72.00

SERIES OF 1950C — SIGNATURES OF SMITH-DILLON
Issued for all Federal Reserve Banks except Atlanta 75.00

SERIES OF 1950D — SIGNATURES OF GRANAHAN-DILLON
Issued for all Federal Reserve Banks 67.50

SERIES OF 1950E — SIGNATURES OF GRANAHAN-FOWLER
Issued only for New York, Chicago, San Francisco 70.00

FIFTY DOLLAR (1963) FEDERAL RESERVE NOTES

(Small Size)   NOTE NO. 116D

SERIES OF 1963, NO NOTES WERE PRINTED
SERIES OF 1963A — SIGNATURES OF GRANAHAN-FOWLER
Issued for all Federal Reserve Banks 67.50

FIFTY DOLLAR (1969) FEDERAL RESERVE NOTES

(WORDING IN GREEN SEAL CHANGED FROM LATIN TO ENGLISH)

NOTE NO. 116E

SERIES OF 1969 — SIGNATURES OF ELSTON-KENNEDY
Issued for all Federal Reserve Banks 65.00

SERIES OF 1969A — SIGNATURES OF KABIS-CONNALLY
Issued for all Federal Reserve Banks 60.00

SERIES OF 1969B — SIGNATURES OF BANUELOS-CONNALLY
Issued for Boston, New York, Philadelphia, Richmond,
Atlanta, Chicago, Dallas 60.00

SERIES OF 1969C — SIGNATURES OF BANUELOS-SHULTZ
Issued for all Federal Reserve Banks 60.00

SERIES OF 1974 — SIGNATURES OF NEFF-SIMON
Issued for all Federal Reserve Banks 57.50

SERIES OF 1977 — SIGNATURES OF MORTON-BLUMENTHAL
Issued for all Federal Reserve Banks 52.50

SERIES OF 1977A — SIGNATURES OF MORTON-MILLER
Issued for all Federal Reserve Banks .... CURRENT

FIFTY DOLLAR NOTES (1918) FEDERAL RESERVE BANK NOTES
(Large Size)

Face Design: Portrait of President Grant to left, Federal Reserve Bank in center, blue seal right.

Back Design: Female figure of Panama between merchant ship and battleship. Plates were made for all 12 Federal Reserve Districts. Only St. Louis bank was issued. Less than 30 notes are known today.

CITY	SERIES	GOVERNMENT SIGNATURES	BANK SIGNATURES	FINE	UNC.
☐ St. Louis	1918	Teehee-Burke	Attebery-Wells	3600.00	10000.00

FIFTY DOLLAR NOTES (1929) FEDERAL RESERVE BANK
(Small Size)

Face Design:
Portrait of Grant center, name of Bank left, brown serial numbers, black letter for Federal Reserve District.

Back Design:
Same as Note No. 110.

BANK	SERIES	SIGNATURES	SEAL	A.B.P.	V. FINE	UNC.
☐ New York	1929	Jones-Woods	Brown	55.00	80.00	175.00
☐ Cleveland	1929	Jones-Woods	Brown	55.00	80.00	175.00
☐ Chicago	1929	Jones-Woods	Brown	55.00	80.00	185.00
☐ Minneapolis	1929	Jones-Woods	Brown	55.00	80.00	235.00
☐ Kansas City	1929	Jones-Woods	Brown	55.00	80.00	185.00
☐ Dallas	1929	Jones-Woods	Brown	55.00	80.00	200.00
☐ San Francisco	1929	Jones-Woods	Brown	55.00	80.00	180.00

$50.00

ONE HUNDRED DOLLAR NOTES

ORDER OF ISSUE

ONE HUNDRED DOLLAR NOTES (1862-1863) U.S. NOTES
(ALSO KNOWN AS LEGAL TENDER NOTE)

(Large Size)

Face Design: Eagle with spread wings left, three discs with "100", red seal numbers.

$100.00

Back Design: Green, two variations of the wording in obligation.

SERIES	SIGNATURES	SEAL	A.B.P.	GOOD	V. FINE	UNC.
☐ 1862	Chittenden-Spinner*	Red	750.00	1250.00	4750.00	20000.00
☐ 1862	Chittenden-Spinner**	Red	750.00	1250.00	4750.00	20000.00
☐ 1863	Chittenden-Spinner**	Red	750.00	1250.00	4750.00	20000.00

*First Obligation: Similar to Note No. 33   **Second Obligation: Shown above.

Face Design: Portrait of President Lincoln

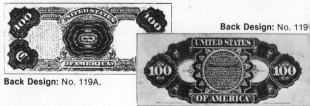

Back Design: No. 119

Back Design: No. 119A.

SERIES	SIGNATURES	SEAL	A.B.P.	GOOD	V. FINE	UNC.
☐1869	Allison-Spinner	Red	1000.00	2500.00	8000.00	25000.00

THE FOLLOWING NOTES HAVE A MODIFIED BACK DESIGN
(Small Size)   **NOTE NO. 119A**

SERIES	SIGNATURES	SEAL	A.B.P.	GOOD	V. FINE	UNC.
☐1875	Allison-New	Sm. Red	475.00	800.00	7500.00	20000.00
☐1875	Allison-Wyman	Sm. Red	450.00	750.00	6500.00	15000.00
☐1878	Allison-Gilfillan	Sm. Red	450.00	750.00	6500.00	15000.00
☐1880	Bruce-Gilfillan	Lg. Brown	450.00	750.00	2475.00	8000.00
☐1880	Bruce-Wyman	Lg. Brown	450.00	750.00	2475.00	8000.00
☐1880	Rosecrans-Jordan	Lg. Red	450.00	750.00	2475.00	8000.00
☐1880	Rosecrans-Hyatt	Lg. Red	450.00	750.00	2475.00	8000.00
☐1880	Rosecrans-Hyatt	Lg. Red	450.00	750.00	2475.00	8000.00
☐1880	Rosecrans-Huston	Lg. Red	450.00	750.00	2475.00	8000.00
☐1880	Rosecrans-Huston	Lg. Brown	450.00	750.00	2475.00	8000.00
☐1880	Tillman-Morgan	Sm. Red	450.00	750.00	2250.00	7000.00
☐1880	Bruce-Roberts	Sm. Red	450.00	750.00	2250.00	7000.00
☐1880	Lyons-Roberts	Sm. Red	450.00	750.00	2250.00	7000.00

ONE HUNDRED DOLLAR NOTES (1966) U.S. NOTES
(ALSO KNOWN AS LEGAL TENDER NOTE)

(Small Size)

Face Design: Portrait of Franklin red seal, red serial numbers.

Back Design: Independence Hall.

SERIES	SIGNATURES	SEAL	V. FINE	UNC.
☐1966*	Granahan-Fowler	Red	120.00	170.00
☐1966A	Elston-Kennedy	Red	115.00	160.00

*This is the first Note to be issued with the new Treasury Seal with wording in English instead of Latin.

Face Design: Perry leaving the Lawrence, left.

Face Design: Border green, center black, Signing of the Declaration of Independence.

SERIES	SIGNATURES	SEAL	A.B.P.	GOOD	V. FINE
☐Original	Chittenden-Spinner	Red	300.00	600.00	4250.00
☐Original	Colby-Spinner	Red	300.00	600.00	4250.00
☐Original	Allison-Spinner	Red	300.00	600.00	4250.00
☐1875	Allison-New	Red	300.00	600.00	4250.00
☐1875	Allison-Wyman	Red	300.00	600.00	4250.00
☐1875	Allison-Gilfillan	Red	300.00	600.00	4250.00
☐1875	Scofield-Gilfillan	Red	300.00	600.00	4250.00
☐1875	Bruce-Gilfillan	Red	300.00	600.00	4250.00
☐1875	Bruce-Wyman	Red	300.00	600.00	4250.00
☐1875	Rosecrans-Huston	Red	300.00	600.00	4250.00
☐1875	Tillman-Morgan	Red	300.00	600.00	4250.00

ONE HUNDRED DOLLAR NOTES (1882) NATIONAL BANK NOTES

SECOND CHARTER PERIOD (Large Size)

NOTE NO. 120A

First Issue—brown seal and brown backs

Face Design: Similar to Note No. 120.
Back Design: Similar to Note No. 39.

SERIES	SIGNATURES	SEAL	A.B.P.	GOOD	V. FINE	UNC.
□ 1882	Bruce-Gilfillan	Brown	250.00	300.00	900.00	2500.00
□ 1882	Bruce-Wyman	Brown	250.00	300.00	900.00	2500.00
□ 1882	Bruce-Jordan	Brown	250.00	300.00	900.00	2500.00
□ 1882	Rosecrans-Jordan	Brown	250.00	300.00	900.00	2500.00
□ 1882	Rosecrans-Hyatt	Brown	250.00	300.00	900.00	2500.00
□ 1882	Rosecrans-Huston	Brown	250.00	300.00	900.00	2500.00
□ 1882	Rosecrans-Nebeker	Brown	250.00	300.00	900.00	2500.00
□ 1882	Rosecrans-Morgan	Brown	250.00	325.00	1000.00	2750.00
□ 1882	Tillman-Morgan	Brown	250.00	300.00	900.00	2500.00
□ 1882	Tillman-Roberts	Brown	250.00	300.00	900.00	2500.00
□ 1882	Bruce-Roberts	Brown	250.00	300.00	900.00	2500.00
□ 1882	Lyons-Roberts	Brown	250.00	300.00	900.00	2500.00

SECOND CHARTER PERIOD (Large Size)

NOTE NO. 121

Second Issue—blue seal, green back with date 1902-1908

Face Design: Similar to Note No. 120.
Back Design: Green with date 1882-1908, center.

SERIES	SIGNATURES	SEAL	A.B.P.	V. FINE	UNC.
□ 1882	Rosecrans-Huston	Blue	400.00	1250.00	3250.00
□ 1882	Rosecrans-Nebeker	Blue	400.00	1250.00	3250.00
□ 1882	Tillman-Morgan	Blue	400.00	1250.00	3250.00
□ 1882	Tillman-Roberts	Blue	400.00	1250.00	3250.00
□ 1882	Bruce-Roberts	Blue	400.00	1250.00	3250.00
□ 1882	Lyons-Roberts	Blue	400.00	1250.00	3250.00
□ 1882	Vernon-Treat	Blue	400.00	1250.00	3500.00
□ 1882	Napier-McClung	Blue	500.00	1750.00	4000.00

This Note was also issued with (value) "ONE HUNDRED DOLLARS" on the back. Very Rare.

$100.00

Face Design: Portrait of John J. Knox, left.

Back Design: Male figures with shield and flags.
First Issue—red seal

SERIES	SIGNATURES	SEAL	A.B.P.	GOOD	V. FINE	UNC.
☐ 1902	Lyons-Roberts	Red	300.00	400.00	1000.00	6000.00
☐ 1902	Lyons-Treat	Red	300.00	400.00	1000.00	6000.00
☐ 1902	Vernon-Treat	Red	300.00	400.00	1000.00	6000.00

Second Issue—design is similar to previous Note. Seal and serial numbers are now blue, back of Note has date 1902-1908 added.

			Blue	150.00	225.00	375.00	750.00

Third Issue—design continues as previous Notes. Seal and serial numbers remain blue, date 1902-1908 removed from back.

The Notes of the **SECOND AND THIRD ISSUE** appeared with various Signatures: LYONS-ROBERTS, LYONS-TREAT, VERNON-TREAT, VERNON-McCLUNG, NAPIER-McCLUNG, PARKER-BURKE, TEEHEE-BURKE, ELLIOTT-BURKE, ELLIOTT-WHITE, SPEELMAN-WHITE, WOODS-WHITE.

			Blue	125.00	175.00	300.00	725.00

Face Design: Portrait of Franklin, center. Name of Bank and City, left. Brown seal, right.

SERIES	SIGNATURES	SEAL	A.B.P.	V. FINE	UNC.
☐ 1929 TYPE I	Jones-Woods	Brown	110.00	160.00	250.00
☐ 1929 TYPE II	Jones-Woods	Brown	115.00	165.00	325.00

ONE HUNDRED DOLLAR NOTES (1878) SILVER CERTIFICATES

SERIES	SIGNATURES	SEAL	A.B.P.	GOOD	V.FINE	UNC.
☐ 1878	Scofield-Gilfillan-White	Red			UNIQUE	
☐ 1878	Scofield-Gilfillan-Hopper	Red		NO SPECIMENS KNOWN		
☐ 1878	Scofield-Gilfillan-Hillhouse	Red		NO SPECIMENS KNOWN		
☐ 1878	Scofield-Gilfillan-Anthony	Red			UNIQUE	
☐ 1878	Scofield-Gilfillan-Wyman	Red		NO SPECIMENS KNOWN		
☐ 1878	Scofield-Gilfillan-Wyman (printed signature of Wyman)	Red	2750.00	4500.00	16000.00	40000.00

SERIES	SIGNATURES	SEAL	A.B.P.	GOOD	V. FINE	UNC.
☐ 1880	Scofield-Gilfillan	Brown		EXTREMELY RARE		
☐ 1880	Bruce-Gilfillan	Brown	1250.00	2500.00	7500.00	19500.00
☐ 1880	Bruce-Wyman	Brown	1250.00	2500.00	7500.00	19500.00
☐ 1880	Rosecrans-Huston	Brown	1200.00	2350.00	7000.00	17500.00
☐ 1880	Rosecrans-Nebeker	Red	1300.00	2650.00	8000.00	22000.00

$100.00

Face Design: Portrait of President Monroe.

SERIES	SIGNATURES	SEAL	A.B.P.	GOOD	V. FINE	UNC.
☐ 1891	Rosecrans-Nebeker	Red	600.00	1400.00	4250.00	13750.00
☐ 1891	Tillman-Morgan	Red	600.00	1400.00	4250.00	13750.00

This Note was also issued in the Series of 1878 and 1880. They are Very Rare.

ONE HUNDRED DOLLAR (1882-1922) GOLD CERTIFICATES
(Large Size)

Face Design: Portrait of Thomas H. Benton.

SERIES	SIGNATURES	SEAL	A.B.P.	GOOD	V. FINE	UNC.
☐ 1882	Bruce-Gilfillan	Lg. Brown	200.00	700.00	1500.00	9000.00
☐ 1882	Bruce-Wyman	Lg. Brown	200.00	700.00	1500.00	9000.00
☐ 1882	Rosecrans-Hyatt	Lg. Red	200.00	700.00	1500.00	9000.00
☐ 1882	Rosecrans-Huston	Lg. Brown	200.00	700.00	1500.00	9000.00
☐ 1882	Lyons-Roberts	Sm. Red	150.00	225.00	375.00	4750.00
☐ 1882	Lyons-Treat	Sm. Red	150.00	225.00	375.00	4750.00
☐ 1882	Vernon-Treat	Sm. Red	150.00	225.00	375.00	4750.00
☐ 1882	Vernon-McClung	Sm. Red	150.00	225.00	375.00	4750.00
☐ 1882	Napier-McClung	Sm. Red	150.00	225.00	375.00	4750.00
☐ 1882	Napier-Thompson	Sm. Red	150.00	225.00	375.00	4750.00
☐ 1882	Napier-Burke	Sm. Red	150.00	225.00	375.00	4750.00
☐ 1882	Parker-Burke	Sm. Red	150.00	225.00	375.00	4750.00
☐ 1882	Teehee-Burke	Sm. Red	150.00	225.00	375.00	4750.00
☐ 1922	Speelman-White	Sm. Red	150.00	225.00	375.00	4750.00

ONE HUNDRED DOLLAR NOTES (1928) GOLD CERTIFICATES
(Small Size)

NOTE NO. 126

Face Design: Portrait of Franklin, center. Yellow seal to left. Yellow numbers.

SERIES	SIGNATURES	SEAL	A.B.P.	GOOD	V. FINE	UNC.
☐ 1928	Woods-Mellon	Gold	110.00	155.00	200.00	625.00

ONE HUNDRED DOLLAR (1890-1891) TREASURY NOTES
(Large Size)

Face Design: Portrait of Commodore Farragut to right.

Back Design: Large "100". This Note is nicknamed "The Watermelon Note" because the zeros on the back resemble watermelons.

SERIES	SIGNATURES	SEAL	A.B.P.	GOOD	V. FINE	UNC.
☐ 1890	Rosecrans-Huston	Brown	1500.00	3000.00	12000.00	RARE
☐ 1891	Rosecrans-Nebeker	Red	2150.00	4500.00	15000.00	RARE

ONE HUNDRED DOLLAR NOTES (1914) FEDERAL RESERVE
(Large Size)

Face Design: Portrait of Franklin in center.
Back Design: Group of five allegorical figures.
SERIES OF 1914 — SIGNATURES OF BURKE-McADOO
RED SEAL AND RED SERIAL NUMBERS

CITY	A.B.P.	GOOD	V.FINE	UNC.	CITY	A.B.P.	GOOD	V.FINE	UNC.
☐Boston . . .	125.00	175.00	300.00	3000.00	☐Chicago . .	125.00	175.00	300.00	3000.00
☐New York	125.00	175.00	300.00	3000.00	☐St. Louis .	125.00	175.00	300.00	3000.00
☐Phil.	125.00	175.00	300.00	3000.00	☐Minn. . . .	125.00	175.00	300.00	3000.00
☐Cleveland .	125.00	175.00	300.00	3000.00	☐Kan. Cy. .	125.00	175.00	300.00	3000.00
☐Richmond .	125.00	175.00	300.00	3000.00	☐Dallas . . .	125.00	175.00	300.00	3000.00
☐Atlanta . . .	125.00	175.00	300.00	3000.00	☐San Fran.	125.00	175.00	300.00	3000.00

SERIES OF 1914—DESIGN CONTINUES AS PREVIOUS NOTE.
THE SEAL AND SERIAL NUMBERS ARE NOW BLUE.
*(This Note was issued with various signatures for each Bank.)

BANK	A.B.P.	V.FINE	UNC.	BANK	A.B.P.	V.FINE	UNC.
☐Boston	110.00	150.00	700.00	☐Chicago	110.00	150.00	700.00
☐New York	110.00	150.00	700.00	☐St. Louis	110.00	150.00	700.00
☐Philadelphia . . .	110.00	150.00	700.00	☐Minneapolis . . .	110.00	150.00	700.00
☐Cleveland	110.00	150.00	700.00	☐Kansas City . . .	110.00	150.00	700.00
☐Richmond	110.00	150.00	700.00	☐Dallas	110.00	150.00	700.00
☐Atlanta	110.00	150.00	700.00	☐San Francisco .	110.00	150.00	700.00

*Signatures: Burke-McAdoo, Burke-Glass, Burke-Huston, White-Mellon.

ONE HUNDRED DOLLAR NOTES (1928)
FEDERAL RESERVE NOTES

(Small Size)

Face Design: Portrait of Franklin. Black Federal Reserve Seal left with number, green Treasury Seal right.

SERIES OF 1928 — SIGNATURES OF WOODS-MELLON, GREEN SEAL

CITY	A.B.P.	V.FINE	UNC.	CITY	A.B.P.	V.FINE	UNC.
☐Boston	105.00	145.00	185.00	☐Chicago	105.00	145.00	185.00
☐New York	105.00	145.00	185.00	☐St. Louis	105.00	145.00	185.00
☐Philadelphia	105.00	145.00	185.00	☐Minneapolis	105.00	145.00	185.00
☐Cleveland	105.00	145.00	185.00	☐Kansas City	105.00	145.00	185.00
☐Richmond	105.00	145.00	185.00	☐Dallas	105.00	145.00	185.00
☐Atlanta	105.00	145.00	185.00	☐San Francisco	105.00	145.00	185.00

SERIES OF 1928A — SIGNATURES OF WOODS-MELLON, GREEN SEAL
NUMBER IN BLACK, FEDERAL RESERVE SEAL IS CHANGED TO A LETTER

(Small Size)

CITY	A.B.P.	V.FINE	UNC.	CITY	A.B.P.	V.FINE	UNC.
☐Boston	105.00	145.00	185.00	☐Chicago	105.00	145.00	185.00
☐New York	105.00	145.00	185.00	☐St. Louis	105.00	145.00	185.00
☐Philadelphia	105.00	145.00	185.00	☐Minneapolis	105.00	145.00	185.00
☐Cleveland	105.00	145.00	185.00	☐Kansas City	105.00	145.00	185.00
☐Richmond	105.00	145.00	185.00	☐Dallas	105.00	145.00	185.00
☐Atlanta	105.00	145.00	185.00	☐San Francisco	105.00	145.00	185.00

SERIES OF 1934—SIGNATURES OF JULIAN-MORGENTHAU, GREEN SEAL

SERIES OF 1934A—SIGNATURES OF JULIAN-MORGENTHAU, GREEN SEAL
(The above two Notes were issued on all Federal Reserve Districts.)

SERIES OF 1934B* — SIGNATURES OF JULIAN-VINSON, GREEN SEAL

SERIES OF 1934C* — SIGNATURES OF JULIAN-SNYDER, GREEN SEAL

SERIES OF 1934D* — SIGNATURES OF CLARK-SNYDER, GREEN SEAL
(*Not all Districts issued in these series.)

	V.FINE	UNC.
AVERAGE PRICES ARE FOR ABOVE FIVE ISSUES	130.00	175.00

ONE HUNDRED DOLLAR NOTES (1950) FEDERAL RESERVE
FEDERAL RESERVE NOTES, GREEN SEAL

(Small Size)

SERIES OF 1950 — SIGNATURES OF CLARK-SNYDER
Issued for all Federal Reserve Banks 152.50

SERIES OF 1950A — SIGNATURES OF PRIEST-HUMPHREY
Issued for all Federal Reserve Banks 142.50

SERIES OF 1950B — SIGNATURES OF PRIEST-ANDERSON
Issued for all Federal Reserve Banks 142.50

SERIES OF 1950C — SIGNATURES OF SMITH-DILLON
Issued for all Federal Reserve Banks 135.00

SERIES OF 1950D — SIGNATURES OF GRANAHAN-DILLON
Issued for all Federal Reserve Banks 135.00

SERIES OF 1950E — SIGNATURES OF GRANAHAN-FOWLER
Issued for New York, Chicago, San Francisco only 145.00

ONE HUNDRED DOLLAR NOTES (1963) FEDERAL RESERVE

SERIES OF 1963 — NO NOTES WERE PRINTED FOR THIS SERIES
SERIES OF 1963A — "IN GOD WE TRUST" ADDED ON BACK
SERIES OF 1963A — SIGNATURES OF GRANAHAN-FOWLER
Issued for all Federal Reserve Banks 125.00

$100.00

ONE HUNDRED DOLLAR NOTES (1969) FEDERAL RESERVE

SERIES OF 1969 — ENGLISH WORDING IN TREASURY SEAL
SERIES OF 1969 — SIGNATURES OF ELSTON-KENNEDY
Issued for all Federal Reserve Banks 120.00

SERIES OF 1969A — SIGNATURES OF KABIS-CONNALLY
Issued for all Federal Reserve Banks 120.00

SERIES OF 1969B — NO NOTES WERE PRINTED
SERIES OF 1969C — SIGNATURES OF BANUELOS-SHULTZ
Issued for all Federal Reserve Banks 120.00

SERIES OF 1974 — SIGNATURES OF NEFF-SIMON
Issued for all Federal Reserve Banks 110.00

SERIES OF 1977 — SIGNATURES OF MORTON-BLUMENTHAL
Issued for all Federal Reserve Banks 110.00

SERIES OF 1977A — SIGNATURES OF MORTON-MILLER
Issued for all Federal Reserve Banks . . . . CURRENT

ONE HUNDRED DOLLAR (1929)
FEDERAL RESERVE BANK NOTES
(ISSUED ONLY IN SERIES OF 1929)

(Small Size)

Face Design: Portrait of Franklin, brown seal and numbers.

Back Design

BANK & CITY	SIGNATURES	SEAL	A.P.B.	V. FINE	UNC.
☐New York	Jones-Woods	Brown	105.00	115.00	250.00
☐Cleveland	Jones-Woods	Brown	105.00	115.00	250.00
☐Richmond	Jones-Woods	Brown	105.00	115.00	275.00
☐Chicago	Jones-Woods	Brown	105.00	115.00	250.00
☐Minneapolis	Jones-Woods	Brown	108.00	125.00	250.00
☐Kansas City	Jones-Woods	Brown	108.00	125.00	290.00
☐Dallas	Jones-Woods	Brown	112.00	115.00	375.00

FIVE HUNDRED, ONE THOUSAND
FIVE THOUSAND and TEN THOUSAND DOLLAR NOTES
(Production of Notes in Denominations above One Hundred Dollars
were discontinued in 1969.)

ORDER OF ISSUE

UNITED STATES NOTES	. . . . $500.00—$1,000.00
NATIONAL BANK NOTES	. . . . $500.00—$1,000.00
SILVER CERTIFICATES	. . . . $500.00—$1,000.00
GOLD CERTIFICATES	. . $500.00—$1,000.00—$5,000.00—$10,000.00
TREASURY OR COIN NOTES	. . . . $1,000.00
FEDERAL RESERVE NOTES	. $500—$1,000.00—$5,000.00—$10,000.00

NOTE: These High Denomination Notes are seldom encountered and rarely collected. Any attempt to list buying and selling prices on them would be purely speculative.

FIVE HUNDRED DOLLAR NOTES (1862) UNITED STATES NOTES
(Large Size)   **NOTE NO. 130**

Face Design: Albert Gallatin.

SERIES	SIGNATURES	SEAL
☐1862	Chittenden-Spinner	Red
☐1863	Chittenden-Spinner	Red

179

FIVE HUNDRED DOLLAR NOTES (1869) UNITED STATES NOTES
(Large Size)

Face Design: Portrait of President Adams.

SERIES	SIGNATURES	SEAL
☐ 1869	Allison-Spinner	Red

FIVE HUNDRED DOLLAR NOTES (1874-1880) U.S. NOTES
(Large Size)

Face Design: General Mansfield.

ISSUED SERIES 1874 — 1875 — 1880
(Various Signatures and Seal Varieties)

FIVE HUNDRED DOLLAR NOTES (1875)
NATIONAL BANK NOTES
FIRST CHARTER ISSUE (Large Size)

Face Design: Defense scene left, name of Bank and City center, steamship right, steamship Sirius.
Back Design: Surrender of General Burgoyne.

SERIES	SIGNATURES	SEAL
☐ Original	Colby-Spinner	Red
☐ 1875	Allison-New	Red

FIVE HUNDRED DOLLAR (1878-1880) SILVER CERTIFICATES
(Large Size)

Face Design: Portrait of Charles Sumner.

SERIES	SIGNATURES	SEAL
☐ 1878 and 1880	Various	Red and Brown

FIVE HUNDRED DOLLAR NOTES (1882) GOLD CERTIFICATES
(Large Size)

Face Design: Portrait of President Lincoln.

SERIES	SIGNATURES	SEAL
☐1882	Various	Various
☐1922	Speelman-White	Red

FIVE HUNDRED DOLLAR NOTES (1928) GOLD CERTIFICATES
(Small Size)

Face Design: Portrait of McKinley, yellow seal to left.

SERIES	SIGNATURES	SEAL
☐1928	Woods-Mellon	Gold

FIVE HUNDRED DOLLAR NOTES (1928-1934)
FEDERAL RESERVE NOTES
(ISSUED BY DIFFERENT BANKS IN VARIOUS SIGNATURES)
(Large Size)

Face Design: Portrait of President McKinley.

SERIES	SIGNATURES	SEAL
☐1928	Woods-Mellon	Green
☐1934 to 1934C	Various	Green

FIVE HUNDRED DOLLAR NOTES (1918)
FEDERAL RESERVE NOTES

(Large Size)

Face Design: Portrait of John Marshall.

SERIES	SIGNATURES	SEAL
☐ 1918	Various	Blue

ONE THOUSAND DOLLAR NOTES (1862-1863) U.S. NOTES
(Large Size)

Face Design: Portrait of Robert Morris.

SERIES	SIGNATURES	SEAL
☐ 1862	Chittenden-Spinner	Red
☐ 1863	Chittenden-Spinner	Red

ONE THOUSAND DOLLAR NOTES (1869-1880) U. S. NOTES
(Large Size)

Face Design: Portrait of DeWitt Clinton.

SERIES	SIGNATURES	SEAL
☐ 1869	Allison-Spinner	Red
☐ 1880	Various	Various

ONE THOUSAND DOLLAR NOTES NATIONAL BANK NOTES
FIRST CHARTER PERIOD (Large Size)

Face Design: Portrait of General Scott left, United States Capitol right, name of Bank and City in center.
Back Design: Washington resigning his commission.

SERIES	SIGNATURES	SEAL
☐ Original	Chittenden-Spinner	Red

ONE THOUSAND DOLLAR NOTES (1880) SILVER CERTIFICATES
(Large Size)

Face Design: Portrait of William L. Marcy left.

SERIES	SIGNATURES	SEAL
☐ 1880	Various	Brown

ONE THOUSAND DOLLAR NOTES (1891) SILVER CERTIFICATES
(Large Size)

SERIES	SIGNATURES	SEAL
☐ 1878 and 1880	Tillman-Morgan	Red

$1000.00

ONE THOUSAND DOLLAR NOTES (1882) GOLD CERTIFICATES
(Small Size)

Face Design: Portrait of Hamilton.

SERIES	SIGNATURES	SEAL
☐ 1882	Various	Various

ONE THOUSAND DOLLAR NOTES (1928) GOLD CERTIFICATES
(Small Size)

Face Design: Portrait of President Cleveland center. yellow seal to left, yellow numbers.

SERIES	SIGNATURES	SEAL
☐ 1928	Woods-Mellon	Yellow

ONE THOUSAND DOLLAR NOTES (1918)
FEDERAL RESERVE NOTES

(Large Size)

Face Design: Portrait of Hamilton.
Back Design: Eagle and flag.

SERIES	SIGNATURES	SEAL
☐ 1918	Various	Blue

ONE THOUSAND DOLLAR NOTES (1928-1934)
FEDERAL RESERVE NOTES

(Small Size)

Face Design: Portrait of President Cleveland.

SERIES	SIGNATURES	SEAL
☐ 1928	Woods-Mellon	Green
☐ 1934	Julian-Morgenthau	Green

FIVE THOUSAND DOLLAR NOTES (1882) GOLD CERTIFICATES
(Large Size)

Face Design: Portrait of President Madison.

SERIES	SIGNATURES	SEAL
☐ 1882	Various	Various

FIVE THOUSAND DOLLAR NOTES (1918) FEDERAL RESERVE
(Large Size)

Face Design: Portrait of President Madison.
Back Design: Washington resigning his commission.

SERIES	SIGNATURES	SEAL
☐ 1918	Burke-Glass	Green

TEN THOUSAND DOLLAR NOTES (1882) GOLD CERTIFICATES
(Large Size)

Face Design: Portrait of President Jackson.

SERIES	SIGNATURES	SEAL
☐ 1882	Teehee-Burke	Gold

TEN THOUSAND DOLLAR NOTES (1928) GOLD CERTIFICATES
(Small Size)

Face Design: Similar to Note No. 141A.

SERIES	SIGNATURES	SEAL
☐ 1928	Woods-Mellon	Gold

TEN THOUSAND DOLLAR NOTES (1928-1934)
FEDERAL RESERVE NOTES

(Small Size)

Face Design: Portrait of Chase.

SERIES	SIGNATURES	SEAL
☐ 1928	Woods-Mellon	Green
☐ 1934	Julian-Morgenthau	Green

ONE HUNDRED THOUSAND DOLLAR NOTE
(1934) GOLD CERTIFICATE

(Small Size)

Face Design:
Portrait of
President
Wilson.

Back Design:
100,000 in
numbers and
Bold Letters.

This is the highest denomination Note printed by the Bureau of Engraving and Printing. This and other Gold Certificates of the 1934 Series were used only for transactions between Federal Reserve Banks. **None were released for general circulation.** Other denominations of the 1934 series were $100—$1,000—$10,000

MULES
(MIXED PLATE NUMBERS)

All United States Currency of every kind and denomination has a plate number on the face and back. These plate numbers are in the lower right corner somewhat close to the fine scroll design. They refer to the number of the engraved plate used to print the sheet of notes. Each plate can be used for about 100,000 impressions. It is then destroyed and a new plate with the next number in sequence is put into use.

During the term of Julian and Morgenthau the plate numbers were changed from almost microscopic to a larger size, more easy to read. Due to this improvement the series designation then in use was an advance on United States Notes, Silver Certificates and Federal Reserve Notes. The signatures remained Julian-Morgenthau. National Currency and Gold Certificates were not affected as these were discontinued earlier.

During the changeover period in printing, plates were sometimes mixed up producing a note with a large number on one side and a small number on the other side. Notes of this variety are called **Mules or Mule Notes.** This is from a term applied to coins struck with the obverse or reverse die of one year and the opposite side from a die of another year.

Many collectors are eager to add one or more of these mule notes to their collection. Some of the most common mule notes are:

$2.00 UNITED STATES NOTES	**$1.00 SILVER CERTIFICATES**
1928-C 1928-D	1935 1935-A

$5.00 UNITED STATES NOTES	**$5.00 SILVER CERTIFICATES**
1928-B 1928-C 1928-D 1928-E	1934 1934-A 1934-B 1934-C

$10.00 SILVER CERTIFICATES

1934   1934-A

Mules were also issued in the Federal Reserve Note series. However, these are not as popular with collectors as the United States Notes and Silver Certificates because of the higher denominations and the 12 districts involved.

Many collectors are eager to add one or more of these mule notes to their collection. Schedule below shows some of the most common mule notes and their values in new condition.

The combination of the Prefix and Suffix letters of the Serial Numbers on Notes is known as Blocks. For instance: A—A Block B—A Block etc.

			UNC.
$2.00 UNITED STATES NOTE	1928-D ...	B — A	300.00
		C — A	25.00
		* — A	40.00

$5.00 UNITED STATES NOTE	1928-B . . .	E — A	80.00
		* — A	400.00
	1928-C	E — A	40.00
		* — A	90.00
$1.00 SILVER CERTIFICATE	1935	N — A Thru P — A	100.00
	1935-A	M — A Thru V — A	30.00
		C — B	55.00
$5.00 SILVER CERTIFICATE	1934-A . . .	D — A Thru G — A	30.00
		* — A	135.00
$10.00 SILVER CERTIFICATE	1934	A — A	45.00
		* — A	85.00
	1934-A	A — A	125.00

Front   **SIZES DIFFERENT**   **Back**

INTRODUCTION TO
UNITED STATES FRACTIONAL CURRENCY

Events following the outbreak of the Civil War resulted in a shortage of circulating coinage. Trade was hampered as many merchants, especially in large cities, were unable to make change and only customers presenting the exact amount for a purchase could buy — but they were generally as short on coins as the shop proprietors. Various attempts were made to solve this problem, by issuing credit slips (which most customers didn't care for), tokens (which they also didn't care for), and using postage stamps as money. Finally in 1862 the government stepped in, recognizing that the economy was being seriously hurt, and issued a series of small paper notes in the equivalent of coinage denominations. They carried designs adapted from the current postage stamps of the day and were known as Postage Currency or Postal Currency. The more popular title is now Fractional Currency. There were five separate issues of fractional currency, three of which occurred during the Civil War and two thereafter, the final one as late as 1874. That a need existed for coin substitutes as late as the 1870's demonstrates the drain placed upon coinage during the war and the long period of recovery. A total of six denominations were issued, from 3¢ to 50¢, comprising 23 designs and more than 100 varieties. Because of its small size and lack of visual impact, fractional currency was long shunned by collectors. In recent years it has enjoyed an unprecedented surge of popularity, which, if continued, promises to drive prices beyond present levels. All told, more than $360,000,000 worth of fractional currency was circulated. It would be extremely plentiful today but for the fact that most notes were redeemed, leaving only about $2,000,000 outstanding. This is what collectors have to work with, and a good deal of **these** are in badly preserved condition.

      FIRST ISSUE — Postage Currency August 21st, 1862
                      5 — 10 — 25 — 50

    SECOND ISSUE — Fractional Currency October 10th, 1863
                      5 — 10 — 25 — 50

      THIRD ISSUE — Fractional Currency December 5th, 1864
              3 — 5 — 10 — 15 — 25 — 50

    FOURTH ISSUE — Fractional Currency July 14th, 1869
               10 — 15 — 25 — 50

      FIFTH ISSUE — Fractional Currency February 26th, 1874
                   10 — 25 — 50

THE FRACTIONAL CURRENCY SHIELD

Fractional Currency Shields were sold by the Treasury Department in 1866. Specimen Notes printed only on one side were used. Very good condition Shields are valued at $1000 to $1500. Choice condition shields in contemporary frames can see for $2500. Shields with pink, green or other colored backgrounds are rare.

UNITED STATES FRACTIONAL CURRENCY
These Notes may be collected by issue or by denomination.
We list them here by denomination for convenience.

NOTE: Since most of these notes were hastily cut from large sheets, the margin size can vary. Specimens with larger than normal margins command premium prices.

THREE-CENT NOTES

THIRD ISSUE   NOTE NO. 142

Face Design:
Portrait of
President Washington.

Back Design:
large "3",
green.

	A.B.P.	GOOD	V.FINE	UNC.
☐ With Light Portrait	7.00	15.00	30.00	100.00
☐ With Dark Portrait	10.00	22.50	40.00	180.00

FIVE-CENT NOTES

FIRST ISSUE   NOTE NO. 143

Face Design:
Portrait of
President Jefferson,
brown

Back Design:
"5" black

	A.B.P.	GOOD	V.FINE	UNC.
☐ Perforated edges. Monogram ABNCO on back	5.00	7.50	32.00	215.00
☐ Perforated edges. Without monogram on back	5.00	12.00	37.00	225.00
☐ Straight edges. Monogram ABNCO on back	4.00	6.00	18.00	85.00
☐ Straight edges. Without monogram on back	6.00	12.00	25.00	120.00

FIVE-CENT NOTES

SECOND ISSUE   NOTE NO. 144

Face Design:
Portrait of
President
Washington

Back Design:
shield and
"5'S", brown.

	A.B.P.	GOOD	V.FINE	UNC.
☐ Value only in bronze on back	5.50	9.00	15.00	100.00
☐ Surcharges 18-63 on back	5.00	9.00	15.00	95.00
☐ Surcharges S-18-63 on back	5.50	9.00	20.00	110.00
☐ Surcharges R-1-18-63 on back Fiber Paper	7.00	14.00	35.00	320.00

UNITED STATES FRACTIONAL CURRENCY
FIVE-CENT NOTES

THIRD ISSUE

NOTE NO. 145

Face Design:
Portrait of
Spencer M. Clark.

Back Design:
green or red

	A.B.P.	GOOD	V.FINE	UNC.
☐Without letter "A" on face. Green back	4.00	7.00	18.00	80.00
☐With letter "A" on face. Green back	4.00	7.00	22.00	85.00
☐Without letter "A" on face. Red back	5.00	8.00	30.00	165.00
☐With letter "A" on face. Red back	7.00	12.00	35.00	175.00

NOTE: This note was authorized to have the portraits of the explorers Lewis and Clark on the face. Mr. Spencer M. Clark, who was then head of the Bureau of Currency, flagrantly placed his own portrait on this Note. This caused Congress to pass legislation forbidding the likeness of any living person on U.S. currency.

TEN-CENT NOTES

FIRST ISSUE

NOTE NO. 146

Face Design:
Portrait of
President Washington.

Back Design:
"10", black

	A.B.P.	GOOD	V.FINE	UNC.
☐Perforated edges. Monogram ABNCO on back	5.00	10.00	30.00	200.00
☐Perforated edges. Without monogram on back	5.00	10.00	32.00	210.00
☐Plain edges. Monogram ABNCO on back	4.00	8.00	15.00	125.00
☐Plain edges. Without monogram on back	6.50	12.00	28.00	185.00

TEN-CENT NOTES

SECOND ISSUE

NOTE NO. 147

Face Design:
Portrait of
President Washington.

Back Design:
"10", green.

	A.B.P.	GOOD	V.FINE	UNC.
☐Value only surcharge on back	4.00	7.00	18.00	100.00
☐Surcharge 18-63 on back	4.00	7.00	18.00	100.00
☐Surcharge S-18-63 on back	4.00	7.00	20.00	95.00
☐Surcharge I-18-63 on back	4.00	8.00	22.00	120.00
☐Surcharge O-63 on back	6.00	10.00	40.00	140.00
☐Surcharge T-I-18-63 on back—fiber paper	6.50	12.00	55.00	300.00

UNITED STATES FRACTIONAL CURRENCY
TEN-CENT NOTES

THIRD ISSUE

NOTE NO. 148

Face Design:
Portrait of
President
Washington.

Back Design:
"10", green or
red.

	A.B.P.	GOOD	V.FINE	UNC.
☐ Printed signatures of Colby-Spinner. Green back . . .	5.00	9.00	20.00	95.00
☐ As above. Figure "1" near left margin on face . . .	5.00	9.00	20.00	90.00
☐ Printed signatures Colby-Spinner. Red back	5.00	12.00	30.00	175.00
☐ As above. Figure "1" near left margin. Red back . .	5.00	12.00	30.00	185.00
☐ Autographed signatures Colby-Spinner. Red back . .	6.00	10.00	35.00	220.00
☐ Autographed signatures Jeffries-Spinner. Red back .	9.00	17.50	50.00	250.00

TEN-CENT NOTES

FOURTH ISSUE

NOTE NO. 149

Face Design:
Bust
of Liberty.

Back Design:
Green with
"Ten" & "10".

	A.B.P.	GOOD	V.FINE	UNC.
☐ Large red seal. Watermarked paper	4.00	7.00	10.00	70.00
☐ Large red seal. Pink fibers in paper	4.00	7.00	12.00	80.00
☐ Large seal. Pink fibers in paper. Right end blue . . .	4.00	7.00	14.00	95.00
☐ Large brown seal	12.00	20.00	75.00	365.00
☐ Small red seal. Pink fibers. Right end blue	4.00	7.00	12.00	80.00

TEN-CENT NOTES

FIFTH ISSUE

NOTE NO. 150

Face Design:
William
Meredith.

Back Design:
Green.

	A.B.P.	GOOD	V.FINE	UNC.
☐ Green seal. Long narrow key	4.00	8.00	15.00	85.00
☐ Red seal. Long narrow key	3.50	5.00	10.00	50.00
☐ Red seal. Short stubby key	3.00	5.00	10.00	55.00

UNITED STATES FRACTIONAL CURRENCY
FIFTEEN-CENT NOTES
FACE AND BACKS PRINTED SEPARATELY

THIRD ISSUE

NOTE NO. 151

Face Design:
Sherman
and President
Grant.

Back Design:
Green
or red.

	NARROW MARGIN	WIDE MARGIN
☐With printed signatures Colby-Spinner*	165.00	300.00
☐With autographed signatures Colby-Spinner**	1000.00	4750.00
☐With autographed signatures Jeffries-Spinner**	240.00	335.00
☐With autographed signatures Allison-Spinner**	260.00	350.00
☐*Green back	150.00	235.00
☐**Red back	150.00	235.00

FIFTEEN-CENT NOTES

FOURTH ISSUE

NOTE NO. 152

Face Design:
Bust
of Columbia.

Back Design:
Green
with "15's".

	A.B.P.	GOOD	V.FINE	UNC.
☐Large seal. Watermarked paper	6.00	12.50	30.00	160.00
☐Large seal. Pink fibers in paper	6.00	12.50	30.00	160.00
☐Large seal. Pink fibers in paper. Right end blue	7.50	15.00	35.00	185.00
☐Large brown seal	12.00	22.00	100.00	425.00
☐Smaller red seal. Pink fibers. Right end blue	7.50	15.00	30.00	150.00

TWENTY-FIVE CENT NOTES

FIRST ISSUE

NOTE NO. 153

Face Design:
Five 5¢
Jefferson Stamps.

Back Design:
Black,
large "25".

	A.B.P.	GOOD	V.FINE	UNC.
☐Perforated edges. Monogram ABNCO on back	6.00	12.50	40.00	120.00
☐Perforated edges. Without monogram on back	7.00	15.00	50.00	145.00
☐Straight edges. Monogram ABNCO on back	5.00	8.50	25.00	100.00
☐Straight edges. Without monogram on back	10.00	20.00	75.00	175.00

UNITED STATES FRACTIONAL CURRENCY
TWENTY-FIVE-CENT NOTES

SECOND ISSUE

(Time and climatic reaction have changed the purple color on the back of this note into many variations.)

Face Design:
Portrait of
President Washington.

Back Design:
Purple
with "25".

	A.B.P.	GOOD	V.FINE	UNC.
☐Value only surcharge on back	5.00	10.00	15.00	150.00
☐Surcharge 18-63 on back	5.00	12.00	20.00	185.00
☐Surcharge A-18-63 on back	5.00	12.00	20.00	170.00
☐Surcharge I-18-63 on back	6.00	12.00	20.00	170.00
☐Surcharge 2-18-63 on back	6.00	12.00	20.00	170.00
☐Surcharge S-18-63 on back	5.00	10.00	18.00	165.00
☐Surcharge T-I-18-63 on back, fiber paper	7.00	15.00	40.00	280.00
☐Surcharge T-2-18-63 on back, fiber paper	7.00	15.00	35.00	260.00
☐Surcharge S-2-18-63, fiber paper		RARE		

TWENTY-FIVE-CENT NOTES

THIRD ISSUE

(All Notes have printed signatures of COLBY-SPINNER.)

Face Design:
Portrait of
Fessenden.

Back Design:
Green or red
with "25 CENTS".

	A.B.P.	GOOD	V.FINE	UNC.
☐Face—Bust of Fessenden between solid bronze surcharges. Fiber paper. Back — Green. Surcharge M-2-6-5 in corners	125.00	200.00	500.00	1750.00
☐As above. With letter "A" in lower left corner of face	150.00	265.00	625.00	2500.00
☐Face—Fessenden. Open scroll bronze surcharges. Fiber paper. Back — Green. Surcharges M-2-6-5 in corners	10.00	20.00	70.00	300.00
☐As above with letter "A" in lower left corners of face	14.00	25.00	65.00	250.00
☐Face—Fessenden. Open scroll surcharges. Plain paper. Back — Green. Value surcharges only	5.00	12.00	32.00	125.00
☐As above. Letter "A" in lower left corner of face. Back — Green. Plain paper	5.00	12.00	25.00	125.00

FRACTIONAL

UNITED STATES FRACTIONAL CURRENCY
TWENTY-FIVE-CENT NOTES

☐ Face — Fessenden. Red back.
  Value surcharge only 6.00   12.00   35.00   175.00
☐ As above. Letter "A" in lower left
  corner of face 8.00   17.50   55.00   210.00

FOURTH ISSUE   **NOTE NO. 156**

Face Design:
Portrait of
President Washington   **Back Design:**
and Treasury Seal.   Green.

	A.B.P.	GOOD	V.FINE	UNC.
☐ Large seal. Plain watermarked paper	5.00	10.00	35.00	90.00
☐ Large seal. Pink silk fiber in paper	5.00	10.00	35.00	85.00
☐ Large seal. Pink fibers in paper. Right end blue	5.00	10.00	35.00	90.00
☐ Large brown seal. Right end blue	25.00	55.00	110.00	450.00
☐ Smaller red seal. Right end blue	5.00	10.00	32.00	85.00

TWENTY-FIVE-CENT NOTES

FIFTH ISSUE   **NOTE NO. 157**

Face Design:
Five 10¢   **Back Design:**
Washington Stamps.   Black.

	A.B.P.	GOOD	V.FINE	UNC.
☐ With long narrow key in Treasury Seal	3.50	7.50	15.00	55.00
☐ With short stubby key in Treasury Seal	3.50	7.50	15.00	55.00

FIFTY-CENT NOTES

FIRST ISSUE   **NOTE NO. 158**

Face Design:
Portrait of
Walker and red seal.   **Back Design:**
                                                     Green.

UNITED STATES FRACTIONAL CURRENCY

	A.B.P.	GOOD	V.FINE	UNC.
☐ Perforated edges. Monogram ABNCO on back . . 8.00		22.00	55.00	310.00
☐ Perforated edges. Without monogram on back . 8.00		22.00	70.00	330.00
☐ Straight edges. Monogram ABNCO on back 6.00		15.00	40.00	175.00
☐ Straight edges. Without monogram 10.00		30.00	70.00	320.00

FIFTY-CENT NOTES

SECOND ISSUE   NOTE NO. 159

Face Design:
Portrait of
President Washington

Back Design:
Red

	A.B.P.	GOOD	V.FINE	UNC.
☐ Value surcharge only in back 60.00		125.00	475.00	1500.00
☐ Surcharge 18-63 on back 7.50		15.00	32.00	360.00
☐ Surcharge A-18-63 on back 5.00		10.00	20.00	325.00
☐ Surcharge I-18-63 . . . . 5.00		10.00	20.00	325.00
☐ Surcharge O-I-18-63. Fiber paper 7.00		15.00	40.00	400.00
☐ Surcharge R-2-18-63. Fiber paper 10.00		20.00	50.00	480.00
☐ Surcharge T-I-18-63. Fiber paper 7.00		12.50	35.00	400.00
☐ Surcharge T-18-63. Fiber paper 15.00		30.00	75.00	470.00

FIFTY-CENT NOTES

THIRD ISSUE   NOTE NO. 160
(NOTES WITH PRINTED SIGNATURES OF COLBY-SPINNER, GREEN BACKS.)

Face Design:
Justice with
Sword,
Shield,
Scales.

Back Design:
Green
or red.

	A.B.P.	GOOD	V.FINE	UNC.
☐ Value surcharge and S-2-6-4 on back.				
Fiber paper			VERY RARE	
☐ Value surcharge and A-2-6-5 on back.				
Fiber paper 17.50		35.00	80.00	365.00
☐ As above with ''1'' and letter ''A'' on face.				
A-2-6-5 on back 35.00		65.00	190.00	475.00
☐ As above with ''1'' only on face.				
A-2-6-5 on back 20.00		40.00	95.00	235.00
☐ As above with letter ''A'' only on face.				
A-2-6-5 on back 18.00		35.00	75.00	235.00

FRACTIONAL

UNITED STATES FRACTIONAL CURRENCY

	A.B.P.	GOOD	V.FINE	UNC.
☐A-2-6-5 on back, narrowly spaced. Plain paper	5.00	9.00	22.00	100.00
☐As above. Numeral "1" and letter "A" on face	14.00	25.00	60.00	200.00
☐As above. Numeral "1" only on face	5.00	8.00	25.00	100.00
☐As above. Letter "A" only on face	10.00	17.00	30.00	125.00
☐A-2-6-5 on back, widely spaced. Plain paper	4.00	8.00	35.00	125.00
☐As above. Numeral "1" and letter "A" on face	12.00	25.00	125.00	420.00
☐As above. Numeral "1" only on face	4.00	8.00	40.00	200.00
☐As above. Letter "A" only on face	5.00	10.00	50.00	235.00
☐Without position letters or back surcharges	4.00	7.50	20.00	80.00
☐As above with numeral "1" and letter "A" on face	12.00	25.00	60.00	200.00
☐As above with numeral "1" only on face	4.00	7.50	25.00	90.00
☐As above with letter "A" only on face	5.00	10.00	30.00	100.00

(NOTES WITH PRINTED SIGNATURES OF COLBY-SPINNER, RED BACKS.)

	A.B.P.	GOOD	V.FINE	UNC.
☐Value surcharge and S-2-6-4 on back. Fiber	65.00	175.00	400.00	875.00
☐As above. Numeral "1" and letter "A"	125.00	250.00	600.00	RARE
☐As above. Numeral "1" only on face	50.00	150.00	425.00	1500.00
☐As above. Letter "A" only on face	75.00	150.00	465.00	1750.00
☐Value surcharge and A-2-6-5 on back Plain	5.00	10.00	30.00	120.00
☐As above. Numeral "1" and letter "A"	12.00	30.00	75.00	250.00
☐As above. Numeral "1" only on face	8.00	14.00	35.00	125.00
☐As above. Letter "A" only on face	8.00	15.00	40.00	150.00
☐Value surcharge only on back. Plain paper	9.00	15.00	35.00	140.00
☐As above. Numeral "1" and letter "A" on face	12.00	25.00	70.00	250.00
☐As above. Numeral "1" only on face	8.00	17.00	40.00	140.00
☐As above. Letter "A" only on face	8.00	20.00	60.00	180.00

(NOTES WITH AUTOGRAPHED SIGNATURES OF COLBY-SPINNER, RED BACKS.)

	A.B.P.	GOOD	V.FINE	UNC.
☐Value surcharge and S-2-6-4 on back. Fiber	40.00	75.00	175.00	625.00
☐Value surcharge and A-2-6-5 on back. Fiber	10.00	20.00	50.00	200.00
☐Value surcharge only on back. Plain paper	8.00	14.00	35.00	145.00

FIFTY-CENT NOTES

THIRD ISSUE

NOTE NO. 161

Face Design:
Bust of
Spinner with
surcharges.

Back Design:
Green
or red.

(NOTES WITH PRINTED SIGNATURES OF COLBY-SPINNER, GREEN BACKS.)

UNITED STATES FRACTIONAL CURRENCY

	A.B.P.	GOOD	V.FINE	UNC.
☐Value surcharge and A-2-6-5 on back	5.00	10.00	35.00	135.00
☐As above. Numeral "1" and letter "A" on face	10.00	25.00	60.00	175.00
☐As above. Numeral "1" only on face	5.00	10.00	35.00	135.00
☐As above. Letter "A" only on face	6.00	12.00	45.00	150.00
☐Value surcharge only on back	4.00	8.00	25.00	65.00
☐As above. Numeral "1" and Letter "A" on face	10.00	20.00	45.00	125.00
☐As above. Numeral "1" only on face	4.00	8.00	25.00	70.00
☐As above. Letter "A" only on face	5.00	10.00	25.00	80.00

TYPE II BACK DESIGN

	A.B.P.	GOOD	V.FINE	UNC.
☐Value surcharge only on back	4.00	7.50	25.00	80.00
☐Numeral "1" and letter "A" on face	10.00	25.00	50.00	150.00
☐Numeral "1" only on face	4.00	8.50	25.00	75.00
☐Letter "A" only on face	5.00	8.50	25.00	90.00

(NOTES WITH PORTRAIT OF SPINNER. PRINTED SIGNATURES OF COLBY-SPINNER, RED BACKS, TYPE I)

	A.B.P.	GOOD	V.FINE	UNC.
☐Value surcharge and A-2-6-5 on back	5.00	8.50	30.00	90.00
☐As above with numeral "1" and letter "A"	10.00	25.00	80.00	250.00
☐As above with numeral "1" only on face	7.00	12.00	30.00	100.00
☐As above with letter "A" only on face	7.00	12.00	40.00	125.00

(NOTES WITH AUTOGRAPHED SIGNATURES, RED BACKS, TYPE I.)

	A.B.P.	GOOD	V.FINE	UNC.
☐Autographed signatures COLBY-SPINNER Back surcharged Value and A-2-6-5	6.00	12.00	30.00	140.00
☐Autographed signatures ALLISON-SPINNER Back surcharged Value and A-2-6-5	10.00	18.00	50.00	200.00
☐Autographed signatures ALLISON-NEW Back surcharged Value and A-2-6-5	285.00	700.00	1500.00	3500.00

FIFTY-CENT NOTES

FOURTH ISSUE

NOTE NO. 162

Face Design:
Bust
of Lincoln.

Back Design:
Green.

	A.B.P.	GOOD	V.FINE	UNC.
☐Plain paper	9.00	18.00	55.00	325.00
☐Paper with pink fibers	10.00	20.00	62.50	365.00

FRACTIONAL

UNITED STATES FRACTIONAL CURRENCY
FIFTY-CENT NOTES

FOURTH ISSUE

NOTE NO. 163

Face Design:
Bust
of Stanton.

Back Design:
Green
with "50".

	A.B.P.	GOOD	V.FINE	UNC.
☐ Red seal and signatures ALLISON-SPINNER. Paper with pink fibers. Blue ends 6.00		10.00	32.50	200.00

FIFTY-CENT NOTES

FOURTH ISSUE

NOTE NO. 164

Face Design:
Bust of
Samuel Dexter.

Back Design:
Green with "50".

	A.B.P.	GOOD	V.FINE	UNC.
☐ Green seal. Pink fibers. Blue ends 6.00		10.00	30.00	160.00

FIFTY-CENT NOTES

FIFTH ISSUE

NOTE NO. 165

Face Design:
Bust
of Crawford.

Back Design:
Green
with "50".

	A.B.P.	GOOD	V.FINE	UNC.
☐ Signatures ALLISON-NEW. Paper with pink fibers. Blue ends 4.50		7.00	15.00	90.00

ERROR OR FREAK NOTES

Notes have been misprinted, from time to time, since the earliest days of currency. The frequency of misprintings and other abnormalities has increased in recent years, due to heavier production and highspeed machinery. This has provided a major sub-hobby for note collectors. Freaks and errors have come into great popularity, their appeal and prices showing upward movement each year.

On the following pages we have pictured and described most of the more familiar and collectible error notes. Pricing is approximate only because many notes bearing the same general type of error differ in severity of error from one specimen to another. As a general rule, the less glaring or obvious errors carry a smaller premium value. Very valuable error notes include double denominations, or bills having the face of one denomination and reverse side of another.

Error and freak notes do turn up in everyday change. Specimens are located either in that fashion or from bank packs. As far as circulated specimens are concerned, some error notes have passed through so many hands before being noticed that the condition is not up to collector standard. This, of course, results in a very low premium valuation.

Values given below are for the specimens pictured and described. Different premiums may be attached to other specimens with similar errors, or notes showing the same errors but of different denominations.

1. MISMATCHED SERIAL NUMBERS

On ordinary notes, the serial number in the lower left of the obverse matches that in the upper right. When it fails to, even by the difference of a single digit, this is known as a MISMATCHED SERIAL NUMBER. It occurs as the result of a cylinder or cylinders in the highspeed numbering machine becoming jammed. If more than one digit is mismatched, the value will be greater.

	V.FINE	UNC.
☐ 1. $1 Federal Reserve Note, Series 1969, Signatures Elston-Kennedy	20.00	50.00

		V. FINE	UNC.
☐ **2.**	$1 Silver Certificate, Series 1957B, Signatures Granahan-Dillon	25.00	60.00

		V. FINE	UNC.
☐ **3.**	$1 Federal Reserve Note, Series 1977A, Signatures Morton-Miller	75.00	200.00

2. INVERTED THIRD PLANT

The inverted third plant is also known as Inverted Overprint. The Treasury Seal, District Seal, Serial Numbers and District Number are inverted on the obverse side of the note, or printed upside-down. Caused by the sheet of notes — having already received the primary design on front and back — being fed upside-down into the press for this so-called "third print." (The back design is the "first print," the front is the "second print," and these various additions comprise the "third print." It is not possible to print these "third print" items at the same time as the obverse design, since they are not standard on every bill. At one time the signatures were included in the "third print" but these are now engraved directly into the plate and are part of the "second print.")

Though very spectacular, inverted third print errors are not particularly scarce and are especially plentiful in 1974 and 1976 series notes.

		V. FINE	UNC.
☐ **4.**	$5 Federal Reserve Note, Series 1974, Signatures Neff-Simon	75.00	125.00

		V. FINE	UNC.
☐ **5.**	$2 Federal Reserve Note, Series 1976, Signatures Neff-Simon	100.00	300.00

ERRORS

		V. FINE	UNC.
☐ **6.**	$1 Federal Reserve Note, Series 1974. Signatures Neff-Simon	65.00	160.00

	V. FINE	UNC.
☐ 7. $50 Federal Reserve Note, Series 1977, Signatures Morton-Blumenthal	200.00	450.00

	V. FINE	UNC.
☐ 8. $20 Federal Reserve Note, Series 1974, Signatures Neff-Simon	100.00	200.00

	V. FINE	UNC.
☐ 9. $10 Federal Reserve Note, Series 1974, Signatures Neff-Simon	90.00	175.00

3. COMPLETE OFFSET TRANSFER

Offset transfers are not, as is often believed, caused by still-wet printed sheets coming into contact under pressure. Though very slight offsetting can occur in that manner, it would not create notes as spectacular as those pictured here, in which the offset impression is almost as strong as the primary printing. These happen as a result of the printing press being started up an instant or so before the paper is fed in. Instead of contacting the paper, the inked plate makes its impression upon the machine bed. When the paper is then fed through, it picks up this "ghost" impression from the bed, in addition to the primary impression it is supposed to receive. Each successive sheet going through the press will acquire the impression **until all ink is totally removed from the machine bed.** But, naturally, the first sheet will show the transfer strongest, and the others will be weaker and weaker. Obviously, the market value of such notes depends largely on the strength of the offset impression. The heavier and more noticeable it is, the more valuable the note will be — all other things being equal.

	V.FINE	UNC.
☐**10.** $5 Federal Reserve Note, Series 1977, Signature Morton-Blumenthal. Offset of reverse side of face.		
☐ Dark	50.00	100.00
☐ Light	20.00	50.00

	V. FINE	UNC.
☐**11.** $1 Federal Reserve Note, Series 1974, Signatures Neff-Simon. Offset of reverse side of face.		
☐ Dark	75.00	150.00
☐ Light	40.00	65.00

4. PARTIAL OFFSET TRANSFER

The most logical explanation for this error is that a sheet of paper fed into the press incorrectly, became mangled or torn, and part of the inked plate contacted the printing press bed. Therefore wet ink was left on those portions of the press bed not covered by paper. When the next sheet was fed through, it received the correct impression plus it acquired a **partial offset transfer** by contacting this wet area of the press bed. Just as with #3 the first sheet going through the press following an accident of this kind will receive the strongest transfer, and it will become gradually less noticeable on succeeding sheets.

		V. FINE	UNC.
☐ **12.**	$1 Federal Reserve Note, Series 1969D, Signatures Banuelos-Schultz. Offset of a portion of reverse side on face.		
☐	Dark	15.00	30.00
☐	Light	10.00	20.00

5. PRINTED FOLD

Notes showing printed folds occur as the result of folds in the paper before printing, which probably happen most often when the sheet is being fed into the press. If the sheet is folded in such a manner that a portion of the reverse side is facing upward, as shown here, it will receive a part of the impression intended for its obverse. Naturally the positioning of these misplaced portions of printing is very random, depending on the nature and size of the fold.

		V. FINE	UNC.
☐ **13.**	$20 Federal Reserve Note, Series 1977, Signatures Morton-Blumenthal. Federal Reserve district seal and district number printed on reverse	75.00	100.00

6. THIRD PRINT ON REVERSE

The cause of this error is obvious, the sheet having been fed through the press on the wrong side (back instead of front) for the third impression or "third print." In the so-called "third print", the note receives the Treasury and Federal Reserve District seals, district numbers and serial numbers.

	V. FINE	UNC.
☐ 14. $1 Federal Reserve Note. Third print on reverse	75.00	175.00

7. BOARD BREAKS

The terminology of this error is misleading. It suggests that the fern-like unprinted areas were caused by a broken printing plate. Actually they must have resulted from something, probably linty matter, sticking to the printing ink. The assumption reached by the public, when it encounters such a note, is that the blank streaks were caused by the paper being folded in printing. This, however, is not possible, as that would yield an error of a much different kind (see PRINTED FOLD).

It should be pointed out that Board Breaks are easily created by counterfeiters by erasing portions of the printed surface, and that the collector ought to examine such specimens closely.

	V. FINE	UNC.
☐ 15. $20 Federal Reserve Note. Board breaks on reverse	40.00	75.00

ERRORS

8. MISSING SECOND PRINT

The "second print" is the front, face or obverse of the note — the "first" print being the reverse or back. A note with Missing Second Print has not received the primary impression on its obverse, though the back is normal and the front carries the standard "third print" matter (Treasury seal, serial numbers, etc.). These errors, while they probably occur pretty frequently, are so easily spotted by B.E.P. checkers that such notes are very scarce on the market.

	V.FINE	UNC.
☐ **16.** $10 Federal Reserve Note. Missing second print	150.00	400.00

9. PRINTED FOLD

This note was folded nearly in half before receiving the "third print," which fell across the waste margin on the reverse side. Had the note not been folded, this waste margin would have been removed in the cutting process. This note, when unfolded, is grotesque in shape.

	V. FINE	UNC.
☐ **17.** $1 Federal Reserve Note. Printed fold with Federal Reserve District seal, district numbers, and serial numbers on reverse. (Naturally, this note lacks the "third print" matter, such as the Treasury seal, that was supposed to appear on the righthand side of the obverse.)	150.00	300.00

V. FINE   UNC.

☐ **18.** $5 Federal Reserve Note. Printed fold with entire Federal Reserve District seal, portion of another Federal Reserve District seal, and portion of two **different** serial numbers on the reverse. It may be hard to imagine how a freak of this nature occurs. This note was folded diagonally along a line bisecting the Lincoln Memorial building slightly to the right of center. The lefthand portion of the reverse side was thereby drawn down across the lefthand side of the **obverse**, extending well below the bottom of the note. It reached far enough down to catch the district seal intended for the note beneath it, as well as a bit of the serial number. This is why the two serial numbers are different; they were supposed to go on two different notes. Obviously, when something this dramatic happens in printing, not only one error note is created buy several — at least — at the same time. Not all necessarily reach circulation however 150.00   300.00

10. THIRD PRINT BLACK INK MISSING OR LIGHT

Though the machinery used is ultra-modern, U.S. currency notes are printed by the same basic technique used when printing was first invented more than 500 years ago. Ink is spread on the metal plates and these are pressed on the sheets as they go through the press. Because the inking is manually fed (as is the paper), an even flow is usually achieved. When an under-inked note is found, it is generally merely "light," giving a faded appearance. But sometimes the plate will be very improperly inked, due to mechanical misfunction or some other cause, resulting in whole areas being unprinted or so lightly printed that they cannot be seen without close inspection. These are not especially valuable notes but **Counterfeit specimens are made.**

ERRORS

211

	V. FINE	UNC.

☐19. $1 Federal Reserve Note, Series 1977. Signatures of Morton-Blumenthal. Federal Reserve district seal and district numbers missing from lefthand side, remainder of ''third print'' material light but distinct. If the lefthand serial number was strong, there might be suspicion of this being a counterfeit 15.00 30.00

11. THIRD PRINT GREEN INK MISSING OR LIGHT

In this case the green rather than the black ink was too lightly applied to the printing plate.

	V. FINE	UNC.

☐20. $5 Federal Reserve Note, Series 1977, Signatures of Morton-Blumenthal. 15.00 30.00

12. NOTE FOLDED DURING OVERPRINT

This note was folded as it was being overprinted and failed to receive the district seal and district numbers at the left side of its obverse. This kind of error, like all involving missing portions of printing, has been extensively counterfeited.

	V. FINE	UNC.
☐ **21.** $2 Federal Reserve Note, Series 1976, Signatures of Neff-Simon	25.00	50.00

13. FAULTY ALIGNMENT

Notes of this kind used to be automatically called "miscut," and sometimes still are. "Faulty alignment" is a more inclusive term which encompasses not only bad cutting but accidents in printing. If the sheet shifts around in the press, it will not receive the printed impressions exactly where they should be. Even if the cutting is normal, the resulting note will be misaligned; the cutting machine cannot correct botched printing. It is **very easy** to determine where the fault lies. If one side of the note has its design higher than the opposite side, this is a printing error. If the misalignment occurs equally on both sides, the problem was in cutting. Since the two sides are not printed in the same operation, it would be a 1-in-a-million chance for them to become equally misaligned.

The value of such notes depends upon the degree of misalignment. Collectors are especially fond of specimens showing a portion — even if very slight, as with the one pictured of an adjoining note.

	V.FINE	UNC.
☐ **22.** $5 Federal Reserve Note. Bottom left of reverse shaved (or "bled"), corresponding portion of adjoining note just visible at top. This ranks as a "dramatic" specimen.		
☐ Slight	15.00	30.00
☐ Dramatic	30.00	75.00

213

14. INSUFFICIENT PRESSURE

Undertinking of the printing plate is not the only cause of weak or partially missing impressions. If the press is not operating correctly and the inked plate meets the sheet with insufficient pressure, the result is similar to underinking. This probably happens as a result of a sheet going through just as the press is being turned off for the day, or at other intervals. Supposedly all action ceases at the instant of turn-off, but considering the rapidity of this operation, it is likely that a random sheet could pass through and be insufficiently impressed. The note pictured here received normal "third prints," as is generally the case with notes whose first or second print is made with insufficient pressure.

	V. FINE	UNC.
☐ **23.** $20 Federal Reserve Note, Series 1977, Signatures of Morton-Blumenthal	50.00	125.00

15. PRINTED FOLD

This note, along with a large portion of the adjoining note, became folded after the second print. When it passed through the press to receive the third print or overprints (seals, serial numbers, etc.), these naturally failed to appear on the folded area.

	V. FINE	UNC.
☐ **24.** $1 Federal Reserve Note. Printed fold with overprints partially missing.		
☐ Small	20.00	40.00
☐ Large	75.00	200.00

16. DOUBLE IMPRESSION

Double impressions have traditionally been blamed on the sheet of notes passing through the press twice, which would be the logical explanation. However, in considering the method by which currency is printed, it would seem more likely that double impression notes have **not** made two trips through the press. They probably result, in most instances, from the automatic paper feed jamming. The sheet just printed fails to be ejected, and the printing plate falls upon it a second time instead of falling on a fresh sheet. This does **not** merely create a strong impression, but a twin or ghost impression, since the sheet is not positioned exactly the same for the second strike. Though the paper feed may not be operating properly, there will still be some slight movement — enough to prevent the second impression from falling directly atop the first.

	V. FINE	UNC.
☐25. $1 Federal Reserve Note, Series 1977A, Signatures of Morton-Miller. Double ''second print'' impression.		
☐ Partial	100.00	200.00
☐ Complete	200.00	1000.00

17. DOUBLE IMPRESSION OF OVERPRINTS ("DOUBLE THIRD PRINT")

This note is normal as far as the primary obverse and reverse printings are concerned. It received twin impressions of the overprints or "third print." This was not caused by jamming of the paper feed as discussed above. Naturally, the serial numbers are different, as the automatic numbering machine turns with every rise and fall of the press.

ERRORS

	V. FINE	UNC.

☐**26.** $20 Federal Reserve Note, Series 1950. Signatures of Priest-Humphrey. Double impression of overprints.

☐   Partial 100.00   300.00
☐   Complete 250.00   750.00

18. THIRD PRINT (OR OVERPRINTS) SHIFTED

Whenever the overprints (serial number, seals, etc.) are out of position, vertically or horizontally, this is known as "third print shifted" or "overprints shifted." In the example pictured, shifting is extreme. This is a premium value specimen which would command the higher of the two sums quoted. Normally, the overprinting on a "shifted" note fails to touch the portrait, or touches it only slightly. The cause of this kind of error is a sheet feeding incorrectly into the press for the overprinting operation. As striking and desirable as these notes are to collectors, they are often unnoticed by the public.

	V.FINE	UNC.

☐**27.** $100 Federal Reserve Note, Series 1969C, Signatures of Banuelos-Schultz. Third print shifted.

☐   Slight 115.00   150.00
☐   Dramatic 125.00   200.00

19. INK SMEAR

Ink smearing is one of the more common abnormalities of currency notes. Generally it can be attributed to malfunction of the automatic inking device which inks the printing plate. When performing properly, ink is applied at a steady controlled pace to the printing plate. A very minor disorder in the machine can dispense enough extra ink to yield very spectacular "smeared notes," such as the one illustrated. The value of ink smear notes depends upon the area and intensity of the smear. They are quite easily faked, so the buyer should be cautious.

	V. FINE	UNC.
☐28. $1 Federal Reserve Note. Ink smear.		
☐ Small	5.00	10.00
☐ Large	15.00	35.00

20. PRINTING FOLD

This note was crumpled along the right side prior to the third printing or application of overprints. Hence the "third print" matter on the lefthand side is normal, but portions of the overprint on the right appear on the note's reverse side.

ERRORS

	V. FINE	UNC.
☐29. $20 Federal Reverse Note, Series 1977, Signatures Morton-Blumenthal	50.00	125.00

21. BLANK CREASE

It occasionally happens that a note becomes creased prior to the reverse or obverse printing, in such a way that a small fold is created. During the printing procedure this fold hides a portion of the note's surface, which therefore fails to receive the impression. These notes are actually double errors, in a way — the cutting machine cuts them without knowledge of the fold, and when the fold is opened out the bill is then of larger than normal size. Since "crease errors" are difficult to spot in the B.E.P.'s checking, they find their way into circulation in rather sizable numbers. It is difficult to place standard values on them because the price depends on exact nature of the specimen. The wider the crease, the more valuable the note will be. Premium values are attached to notes with multiple creases that cause the blank unprinted area to fall across the portrait.

	V. FINE	UNC.
☐ 30. Blank crease Note, any denomination. Value stated is collector premium over and above face value (if note has additional value because of series, signatures, etc., this too must be added).		
☐ Single crease	2.00	10.00
☐ Multiple crease	10.00	30.00

22. MIXED DENOMINATION

These two notes are normal in themselves, and if they were not owned together as a set, no premium value would be attached to them. The error (which may be dubious to term as such) lies with their serial numbers. The $5 note has a serial number one digit higher than the $1, suggesting that it was fed into the printing machine intended to print overprints (or "third prints") on $1 bills. Even when this does happen, which is probably infrequent, it is very difficult to obtain "matching" notes of the kind illustrated, in which the serial numbers are only a single digit apart. Even if you had a $5 note and $1 note (or other combination of denominations) from sheets that were fed one after the other, the odds on getting one-digit-apart serial numbers are extremely small.

The value is given for an Uncirculated set only, as there would be no possibility of finding such matched notes except in a bank pack. Once released into circulation, they can never again be mated.

UNC.

☐**31.** Mixed denomination pair from bank pack, $5 Federal
Reserve Note within pack of $1 Federal Reserve notes 500.00

BLANK REVERSE

U.S. currency has its reverse printed before the obverse — in other
words, back before front. The only logical explanation for blank reverse
notes is that blank paper found its way into the batch of sheets on which
reverses had already been printed. They were then fed — without detection
— into the press for application of the obverse. They continued to escape
notice during printing of the overprints, and very miraculously got into circulation.

	V.FINE	UNC.
☐**32.** $100 Federal Reserve Note. Blank reverse	150.00	400.00

	V. FINE	UNC.
☐**33.** $20 Federal Reserve Note, Series 1977, Signatures of Morton-Blumenthal. Blank reverse	75.00	200.00

☐ **34.** $10 Federal Reserve Note, Series 1974, Signatures of Neff-Simon. Blank reverse

	V. FINE	UNC.
	60.00	150.00

☐ **35.** $1 Federal Reserve note, Series 1977, Signatures of Morton-Blumenthal. Blank reverse

	V. FINE	UNC.
	50.00	125.00

24. DOUBLE DENOMINATION COUNTERFEIT

This is a COUNTERFEIT or faked error. We include it simply to show the kind of work done by counterfeiters, and how such items can be made to resemble genuine errors. This happens to be a counterfeit of an error note **that cannot exist** in genuine state. Thus, there can be no hesitancy in proclaiming it a fake. Anyone who is even slightly familiar with the way currency is printed should instantly recognize this item as a fraud. Nevertheless, fakers succeed in selling (often at high prices) specimens of this kind, probably because some collectors want the impossible for their albums. **Genuine** double or twin denomination notes have the **obverse** of one denomination and the **reverse** of a different denomination. They do not consist of two obverses or two reverses, such as the one pictured. The note illustrated carries four serial numbers. For it to be genuine, it would have had to pass through the "third print" (overprinting) process twice. Obviously it was made by gluing a $1 and $5 note together. Much more deceptive paste-ups, with the notes correctly paired so that obverse of one and reverse of the other shows, are made. Beware!

25. INVERTED OBVERSE

U.S. currency is printed reverse first. Therefore, when the back and front do not face in the same vertical direction (as they should), the note is known as an INVERTED OBVERSE. The term "inverted reverse" is never used. This, of course, results from the sheet being fed through upside-down for the obverse or second print. Though these specimens are scarce in uncirculated condition, they often pass through many hands in circulation before being spotted. The uninformed public is not even aware that a note with faces in opposite directions is an error and has premium value.

	V. FINE	UNC.
☐36. $2 Federal Reverse Note, Series 1976, Signatures of Neff-Simon. Inverted obverse	100.00	250.00

26. MISSING THIRD PRINT

Also known as **missing overprint**. Note released into circulation without having gone through the "third print" operation.

ERRORS

	V. FINE	UNC.
☐ **37.** $1 Federal Reserve Note, Series 1977, Signatures Morton-Blumenthal. Missing third print	75.00	150.00

27. FOREIGN MATTER ON OBVERSE

Sometimes foreign matter, usually paper scraps of one kind or another, gets between the printing plate and the sheet. This naturally results in the area covered by such matter being blank on the note. Because of the extreme pressure exerted in printing, the foreign matter is occasionally "glued" to the note and travels with it into circulation. If the appendage is paper, it will normally be found to be of the same stock from which the note is made — apparently a shred from one of the sheet margins that worked its way into a batch of sheets awaiting printing. **The value of such notes varies successfully,** depending on the size of the foreign matter and its placement. It's **rare** to find notes in which foreign matter became attached before the first or second print. Nearly always, they found their way to the note after the second print and before the third.

	V. FINE	UNC.
☐ **38.** $1 Federal Reserve Note, Series 1974, Signatures Neff-Simon. Foreign matter on obverse	50.00	90.00

	V. FINE	UNC.

☐**39.** $1 Silver Certificate, Series 1935E. Signatures of Priest-Humphrey. Foreign matter on obverse. More valuable than the preceding because of the note's age and the foreign matter being larger 300.00   600.00

28. MISSING PORTION OF REVERSE DESIGN (DUE TO ADHERENCE OF SCRAP PAPER)

In this instance, the foreign matter got in the way of the first print, or reverse printing. It prevented the covered area from being printed, but it **later became dislodged** and is no longer present. What appears on the illustration to be a strip of paper on the note is really the blank unprinted area once covered by the strip. Obviously a note that merely had a random strip of paper attached, over a normally printed design, would have no collector interest.

	V.FINE	UNC.

☐**40.** $1 Federal Reserve Note. Missing portion of reverse design due to adherence of scrap paper 50.00   90.00

29. OVERPRINT PARTIALLY MISSING

The overprint or third print on this note is normal on the righthand side and missing entirely on the left. This was caused by the note being folded (more or less in half, vertically) immediately before overprinting. Had the lefthand side been folded **over the face,** this would have interfered with the overprints on the righthand side. Instead, this specimen was folded **over the reverse side,** or downward, with the result that the missing portion of overprint did not strike the note at all — it simply hit the printing press bed. The reverse side of this note is normal.

	V. FINE	UNC.
☐**41.** $1 Federal Reserve Note, Series 1963A. Overprint partially missing	25.00	50.00

30. THIRD PRINT OFFSET ON REVERSE

This note is normal on the obverse but carries an "offset" of the third print or overprints on its reverse. It would appear that the overprints are showing through to the reverse, as if the note were printed on very thin paper. Actually, this "mirror image" is caused by a malfunction in the printing or paper-feeding machinery. The inked plate for printing the overprints contacted the machine bed without a sheet of paper being in place. Therefore, as the next sheet came through it received the normal overprint on its face and picked up the offset impression on its reverse from the machine bed. Each successive sheet going through the press also received an offset, but it naturally became fainter and fainter as the ink was absorbed. The value of a note of this kind depends on the intensity of impression.

	V. FINE	UNC.
☐**42.** $5 Federal Reserve Note. Offset impression of overprints on reverse	100.00	250.00

31. "SWOLLEN HEAD" CREASE

Notes with blank unprinted streaks, caused by folds in the paper prior to printing, are often valued according to the effect they create on the portrait. In this specimen Washington has received a swollen head. A blank crease extending the entire length of the note, such as this, is unusual.

	V. FINE	UNC.
☐ **43.** $1 Federal Reserve Note, Series 1974, Signatures of Neff-Simon. Long diagonal "swollen head" crease	20.00	50.00

32. OVERPRINT ON ACCOMPANYING FOREIGN MATTER

The large piece of paper pictured atop this note is not attached to it. It became lodged between the printing plate and sheet at the time of printing the "third print." It was subsequently dislodged but traveled along with the note into circulation. This is an extremely unusual and valuable error, as the accompanying foreign matter contains the **entire overprint.** The note is normal except that it lacks the overprints.

	V. FINE	UNC.
☐ **44.** $20 Federal Reserve Note. Overprint on accompany foreign matter	*	1000.00

★ No "Very Fine" price is given because this note and the accompanying scrap paper would have to be spotted in a bank pack. After reaching circulation, the two pieces would obviously not travel together.

33. DRAMATIC THIRD PRINT SHIFT

The sheet from which this note came, entered the printing press (to receive its overprintings) badly aligned. It was shifted to nearly a 45-degree angle and missed a substantial portion of the overprint intended for its righthand side. At the same time it picked up part of the overprint intended for the adjoining note. This is about as "dramatic" as a Dramatic Third Print Shift can get.

		V. FINE	UNC.
☐**45.** $1 Federal Reserve Note, Series 1974, Signatures of Neff-Simon		200.00	500.00

34. CUTTING ERROR

This note, normal in other respects, became folded after all printing was completed but prior to cutting. When cut, the automatic B.E.P. cutting machine naturally treated it as a regular note and cut it in the standard fashion. But because of the fold, the cutting yielded a bill of much larger than normal size, showing a substantial portion of a neighboring bill at the top and a small portion of one below. Though cutting errors are not uncommon, one as gross as this certainly is.

		V.FINE	UNC.
☐**46.** $2 Federal Reserve Note. Cutting error		*	1000.00

*No "Very Fine" valuation is given, as such a specimen would not, conceivably, go into general circulation from a bank pack without being noticed.

35. TEST IMPRESSIONS

Also known as "trial impressions." A better name would probably be "essays" (to borrow from the language of stamp collecting). These unusual pieces were printed in Germany to test the C.O.P.E. press. They were supposed to all be destroyed but, as was the case with aluminum trial pennies struck several years ago, a few survived. The Treasury Department has not, apparently, published any ruling on the legality of owning such material. Private collectors should realize that such items could be declared illegal to own, and subject to confiscation.

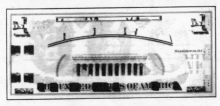

		UNC.
☐47.	Test note.	
☐	Green & black	250.00
☐	Maroon & black	350.00
☐	Brown & black	350.00

227

CONFEDERATE MONEY

The Civil War Centennial of 1861-65 has generally been credited with sparking a rise of interest in the collecting and study of Confederate or C.S.A. notes. This, however, is not totally borne out by facts, as C.S.A. currency had advanced steadily in value since the 1940's. It rides a crest of popularity today well surpassing the early 1960's. This is due in part to the exhaustive research carried out since that time and numerous books and articles published. Even today, some C.S.A. notes would still appear to be undervalued based on their availability vs. regular U.S. issues.

History. It became apparent upon the outbreak of the Civil War that both sides would experience extreme coinage shortages and each took to the printing of notes that could be exchanged in lieu of bullion or "real money" (which, we must understand, always meant coined money until the 1860's). The South suffered more serious difficulties than the North, as it did not have as many skilled printers or engravers at its command. Also, with the war being fought on its territory rather than the North's, there was an ever-present danger of sabotage to plants printing money or engaging in related activities. The Confederacy tried by all available means to satisfy the currency demand, and succeeded in distributing quite a large quantity of notes. Its shortage was taken up by notes issued by private banks, individual states, counties, railroads, and private merchants. Merchant tokens, to take the place of rapidly disappearing small change, poured forth in abundance during this period. All told, the Confederate Congress authorized the printing of about one and a half billion dollars worth of paper currency. It is impossible to determine the total actually produced but it would appear that this figure was far surpassed. At the war's conclusion, these notes were worthless as the C.S.A. no longer existed and the federal government refused to redeem them. Many were undoubtedly discarded as scrap but a surprising number were held faithfully by their owners, who believed "the South will rise again." The South did indeed rise, industrially and economically, and those old C.S.A. notes rose too. They still aren't spendable but many are worth sums in excess of face value as collectors' pieces. Until about 1900, however, practically no value was placed on Confederate currency — even by collectors.

Designs. Some surprising designs will be observed, including mythological gods and goddesses that seem to relate very little to the South's artistic or cultural climate of the 1860's. Many scholarly efforts have been made to explain away the use of such motifs but the simple fact is that they appeared not so much by choice as necessity. Southern printers, not having the facilities of their Northern counterparts, were compelled to make do with whatever engravings or "stock cuts" were already on hand, as inappropriate as they might have proved. However, a number of original designs were created reflecting unmistakably regional themes and at times picturing heros or leaders of the Confederacy. Slaves at labor, used as a symbol of the South's economic strength and its supposed advantage over the North, where labor was hired, was a frequent motif.

Sailors were also depicted, as well as railroad trains and anything else that appeared symbolic of Southern industry. Probably the most notable single design, not intended to carry the satirical overtones it now possesses, is "General Francis Marion's Sweet Potato Breakfast" on the $10 1861. In general, the C.S.A. notes are not so badly designed a group as might be anticipated in light of conditions. The designing, was in fact, several leagues improved over the printing, which often left much to be desired. George Washington is depicted — not for being the first U.S. President but as a native son of Virginia. Jefferson Davis, President of the C.S.A., is among the more common portraits. He became even more disliked in the North than he otherwise might have been, because of his picture turning up on currency. But after the war he took a moderate stand and erased the old ill feelings; he even had words of praise for Lincoln. Other individuals whose portraits (not necessarily very faithful) will be encountered are:

John C. Calhoun, U.S. Senator who led the battle for slavery and Southern Rights (later called "states rights").

Alexander H. Stephen, Davis' Vice-President of the C.S.A.

Judah P. Benjamin, holder of various official titles in the Southern government.

C. G. Memminger, Secretary of the Treasury and Secretary of War.

Lucy Pickens, wife of South Carolina's governor and the only woman (aside from mythological types) shown on C.S.A. currency.

John E. Ward.

R. M. T. Hunter.

Printers. The study of printers of C.S.A. notes is complex, made no less so by the fact that some contractors produced only plates, others did only printing (from plates procured elsewhere), while some did both. The principal Southern printer was the lithography firm of Hoyer & Ludwig of Richmond, Virginia. Also located at Richmond were Keatinge & Ball, which did commendable if not exactly inspired work, and B. Duncan, who also worked at Columbia, South Carolina. Another firm involved in quite a bit of note printing was J. T. Paterson of Columbia. The so-called "Southern Bank Note Company" was a fictitious name used to disguise the origin of notes prepared in the North. Some early notes were marked "National Bank Note Co., New York," but it was subsequently decided to remove correct identification from the notes of this printer, undoubtedly on the latter's request (fearing prosecution for aiding the enemy).

Cancellations. Two varieties of cancels are commonly found on C.S.A. notes. First is the cut cancel (CC), in which a knife or similar instrument has been used to make piercings in a design or pattern. Unless roughly executed, such cuts do not materially reduce a specimen's value. In the case of some notes, examples without cancellation are almost impossible to find. The COC or Cut Out Cancel is more objectionable because, instead of merely leaving slits, a portion of the paper was removed. The reduction of value for a Cut Out Cancel averages around 25 percent. These are considered "space fillers" if the issue is fairly common, but a rare note with a COC may be very desirable. Pen Cancellations (PC) are far less frequently encountered. These show the word "Canceled" written out by hand across the note's face, in ink. Unless the ink is heavy or blotchy, a pen cancel will not have too much bearing on value. As the note is not physically injured, it would seem to be the least offensive of the three varieties. Whenever a note is being sold, presence of a cancel, or whatever type, should be plainly spelled out. Some collectors are not interested in canceled specimens. In time, as the scarce issues become even scarcer, they will probably have to be accepted as a fact of life.

Signatures. There are so many signature combinations on C.S.A. notes that utter confusion would await anyone attempting to collect them on this basis. The names are unknown and in most instances difficult to trace, representing not government officials but employees authorized to sign for the Treasurer and Registrar of the Treasury. Only the first six notes bear the actual signatures of these officials.

Condition Grades. While condition standards are basically the same for Confederate currency as other notes of their age, some allowance must be made for paper quality and deficiencies in printing and cutting. These matters have nothing to do with the **preservation** or wear and can be observed just as frequently in uncirculated specimens as those in average condition. Without a source of good paper, printers were obliged to use whatever was most easily and quickly obtainable. Often the paper was thin, or stiff, or contained networks of minute wrinkles which interfered somewhat with printing. Cutting was generally not done by machine, as in the North, but by hand with a pair of scissors — workers actually took the sheets and cut them apart notes individually. When paper-cutting devices were employed, they were apparently not of the best quality. In any case, regular edges on C.S.A. notes are uncommon and their absence does not constitute grounds for classifying an otherwise perfect specimen in a condition grade below Uncirculated. When the occasional gem is located — a well-printed, well-preserved note on good paper, decently cut — its value is sure to be higher than those listed. The collecter is not advised to confine himself to such specimens, as his activities would become seriously limited.

UNCIRCULATED · UNC. An uncirculated note shows no evidence of handling and is as close to "new condition," as possible. An uncirculated specimen may, however, have pinholes or a finger smudge, which should be mentioned in a sales offering. If these are readily noticeable, the note deserves to be classified as "almost uncirculated." Crispness is hardly a criterion of uncirculation as this quality is expected in notes graded as low as Very Fine.

ALMOST UNCIRCULATED · A.U. Similar to the above grade but not quite as good as an uncirculated specimen. The note bears no indication of having actually circulated but has minor flaws resulting from accident or mishandling, such as counting crinkles.

EXTREMELY FINE · X.F. An X.F. note is on the borderline between uncirculated and circulated. It has not been heavily handled but may reveal several imperfections: a pinhole, finger smudge, counting crinkles, or a light wallet fold. The fold is not so heavy as to be termed a crease.

VERY FINE · V.F. Has been in circulation but is not worn or seriously creased. It must still be clean and crisp, without stains or tears. Fine to Very Fine condition is considered the equivalent of "average circulated" but not "average condition" (which is another term for **poor**).

FINE · F. A note that has been in circulation and shows it, but has no physical injuries or just slight ones.

VERY GOOD · V.G. A well-circulated note bearing evidence of numerous folding. It may possibly have creased corners and wrinkles as well as light staining, smudging, or pinholes, but major defects (such as a missing corner) would place it into an even lower category.

GOOD · G. Heavily circulated, worn, possibly stained or scribbled on, edges could be frayed or "dog-eared." There may be holes larger than pin-punctures, but not on the central portion of design. This is the lowest grade of condition acceptable to a collector, and only when nothing better is available. Unless very rare, such specimens are considered space-fillers only.

A.B.P. · AVERAGE BUYING PRICES. The average buying prices given here are the approximate sums paid by retail dealers for specimens in good condition. As selling prices vary, so do buying prices, and in fact they usually vary a bit more. A dealer overstocked on a certain note is sure to offer less than one who has no specimens on hand. The dealer's location, size of operation and other circumstances will also influence the buying price. We present these figures merely as rough guides.

CONFEDERATE STATES OF AMERICA — 1861 ISSUE
MONTGOMERY, ALABAMA
$1,000,000 Authorized by Act of "March 9th". Written Dates "1861".

"NATIONAL BANK NOTE CO., NY."

T1

Face Design: Green and black, bears "Interest Ten Cents Per Day", 607 issued. John C. Calhoun left, Andrew Jackson right.

CRISWELL # ☐1	NOTE $1000	A.B.P. 2000.00	GOOD 3000.00	UNC. 6500.00

"NATIONAL BANK NOTE CO., NY."

T2

Face Design: Green and black, bears "Interest Five Cents Per Day", 607 issued. Cattle crossing a brook.

CRISWELL # ☐2	NOTE $500	A.B.P. 2000.00	GOOD 3250.00	UNC. 6250.00

"NATIONAL BANK NOTE CO., NY."

T3

Face Design: Green and black, bears "Interest One Cent Per Day". Railway train, Minerva left.

CRISWELL #	NOTE		A.B.P.	GOOD	UNC.
□3	$100	....	750.00	1400.00	2800.00

"NATIONAL BANK NOTE CO., NY."

T4

Face Design: Green and black, bears "Interest Half A Cent Per Day". Negroes hoeing cotton.

CRISWELL #	NOTE		A.B.P.	GOOD	UNC.
□4	$50	....	600.00	1250.00	2000.00

CONFEDERATE

CONFEDERATE STATES OF AMERICA—1861 ISSUE

AMERICAN BANK NOTE CO., NY."
(Though ostensibly by the "SOUTHERN BANK NOTE CO.")

T5

Face Design: Green and black, red fibre paper, bears "Interest One Cent Per Day". Railway train, Justice left and Minerva right.

CRISWELL #	NOTE		A.B.P.	GOOD	UNC.
☐5	$100		75.00	150.00	300.00

T6

Face Design: Green and black, red fibre paper, bears "Interest Half A Cent Per Day". Pallas and Ceres seated on bale of cotton, Washington at right.

CRISWELL #	NOTE		A.B.P.	GOOD	UNC.
☐6	$50		65.00	95.00	250.00

CONFEDERATE STATES OF AMERICA—1861 ISSUE

$20,000,000 Authorized by Act of "May 16th, 1861"

"HOYER & LUDWIG, RICHMOND, VA."
(All Lithographic Date "July 25th, 1861")

T7

Face Design: Ceres and Proserpina flying, Washington left.

CRISWELL #	NOTE		A.B.P.	GOOD	UNC.
☐ 7-13	$100		75.00	110.00	250.00

T8

Face Design: Washington, Tellus left.

CRISWELL #	NOTE		A.B.P.	GOOD	UNC.
☐ 14-22	$50		9.00	22.00	40.00

CONFEDERATE STATES OF AMERICA—1861 ISSUE

Face Design: Exists in a variety of colors with plain and printed fancy reverses.

☐21	$20	....	$12.00	20.00	65.00

NOTE: The above type notes were bogus. For years it was thought they were a regular Confederate issue, and evidence exists that they were circulated as such. No collection of Confederate notes is complete without one. There is no evidence as to who the printer was, but the authors have reason to believe he was located somewhere in Ohio. It is not a product of S. C. Upham, of Philadelphia, the well-known counterfeiter of Confederate notes.

T9

Face Design: Large sailing vessel, "20" at left.

CRISWELL #	NOTE		A.B.P.	GOOD	UNC.
☐23-33	$20	....	6.00	12.00	35.00

T10

Face Design: Liberty seated by Eagle, with shield with flag.

NOTE: There are at least 42 minor varieties of this note, including a supposed 10 or 11 stars on shield. Usually the stars are so indistinct that a note may show from six to 15 stars. The other differences are in minute changes in the size of the ''10'' in the upper corners. We list only the major type.

CRISWELL #	NOTE	A.B.P.	GOOD	UNC.
☐ 34-40	$10	10.00	18.00	200.00

T11

Face Design: Liberty seated by Eagle, sailor left.

CRISWELL #	NOTE	A.B.P.	GOOD	UNC.
☐ 42-44	$5	80.00	150.00	5000.00

CONFEDERATE STATES OF AMERICA—1861 ISSUE

"J. MANOUVRIER, NEW ORLEANS"
(Written Date "July 25th, 1861")

T12

Face Design: "Confederate States of America" in blue on blue reverse.

CRISWELL # □ 46-49	NOTE $5	A.B.P. 125.00	GOOD 350.00	UNC. 2750.00

$100,000,000 authorized by Act of "Aug. 19th, 1861".
$50,000,000 authorized by Act of "Dec. 24th, 1861".

"HOYER & LUDWIG, RICHMOND, VA."
(Lithographic Date, "September 2nd, 2d, & s, 1961".)

T13

Face Design: Negros loading cotton, sailor left.

CRISWELL # □ 50-58	NOTE $100	A.B.P. 6.50	GOOD 12.00	UNC. 35.00

CONFEDERATE STATES OF AMERICA—1861 ISSUE

T14

Face Design: Moneta seated by treasure chests; sailor left.

CRISWELL #	NOTE	A.B.P.	GOOD	UNC.
☐ 59-78	$50	6.00	9.00	25.00

"SOUTHERN BANK NOTE CO., NEW ORLEANS"

T15

Face Design: Black and red on red fibre paper. Railway train, Justice right, Hope with anchor left.

CRISWELL #	NOTE	A.B.P.	GOOD	UNC.
☐ 79	$50	200.00	400.00	2000.00

CONFEDERATE STATES OF AMERICA—1861 ISSUE

"KEATINGE & BALL, RICHMOND, VA."

 T16

Face Design: Black and green, red fibre paper. Portrait of Jefferson Davis.

CRISWELL #	NOTE		A.B.P.	GOOD	UNC.
☐80-94	$50	....	9.00	15.00	60.00

"HOYER & LUDWIG, RICHMOND, VA."

T17

Face Design: Black with green ornamentation, plain paper. Ceres seated between Commerce and Navigation, Liberty left.

CRISWELL #	NOTE		A.B.P.	GOOD	UNC.
☐99-100	$20	....	40.00	75.00	200.00

CONFEDERATE STATES OF AMERICA—1861 ISSUE

"HOYER & LUDWIG, RICHMOND, VA."

T18

Face Design: Large sailing vessel, sailor at capstan left.

CRISWELL #	NOTE		A.B.P.	GOOD	UNC.
☐ 101-136	$20	. . . .	2.00	4.00	20.00

"SOUTHERN BANK NOTE CO., NEW ORLEANS"

T19

Face Design: Black and red on red fibre paper. Navigation seated by charts, Minerva left, blacksmith right.

CRISWELL #	NOTE		A.B.P.	GOOD	UNC.
☐ 137	20	. . . .	110.00	200.00	1600.00

CONFEDERATE STATES OF AMERICA—1861 ISSUE

T20

Face Design: Industry seated between cupid and beehive, bust of A. H. Stevens left.

PRINTED BY "B. DUNCAN, COLUMBIA, SC."

CRISWELL #	NOTE	A.B.P.	GOOD	UNC.
☐ 139-140	$20	3.50	8.00	35.00

PRINTED BY "B. DUNCAN, RICHMOND, VA."

☐ 141-143	$20	3.00	5.00	30.00

"KEATINGE & BALL, COLUMBIA, SC."

T21

Face Design: Portrait of Alexander H. Stephens.

YELLOW GREEN ORNAMENTATION

CRISWELL #	NOTE	A.B.P.	GOOD	UNC.
☐ 144	$20	9.00	16.00	180.00

DARK GREEN ORNAMENTATION

☐ 145-149	$20	10.00	15.00	175.00

CONFEDERATES STATES OF AMERICA—1861 ISSUE

"SOUTHERN BANK NOTE CO., NEW ORLEANS"

T22

Face Design: Black and red, red fibre paper. Group of indians, Thetis left, maiden with "X" at right.

CRISWELL #	NOTE	A.B.P.	GOOD	UNC.
☐150-152	$10	40.00	80.00	200.00

"LEGGETT, KEATINGE & BALL, RICHMOND, VA."

T23

Face Design: Black and orange red. Wagonload of cotton, harvesting sugar cane right. John E. Ward left.

CRISWELL #	NOTE	A.B.P.	GOOD	UNC.
☐153-155	$10	80.00	150.00	550.00

CONFEDERATE STATES OF AMERICA—1861 ISSUE

"LEGGETT, KEATINGE & BALL, RICHMOND, VA."

T24

Face Design: Black and orange red. R. M. T. Hunter left, vignette of child right.

CRISWELL #	NOTE		A.B.P.	GOOD	UNC.
☐156-160	$10	....	10.00	30.00	120.00

"KEATINGE & BALL, RICHMOND, VA."

☐161-167	$10	....	9.75	25.00	110.00

"KEATINGE & BALL, RICHMOND, VA."

T25

Face Design: Hope with anchor, R. M. T. Hunter left, C. G. Memminger, right.

CRISWELL #	NOTE		A.B.P.	GOOD	UNC.
☐168-171	$10	....	9.00	15.00	100.00

CONFEDERATE STATES OF AMERICA—1861 ISSUE

"KEATINGE & BALL, RICHMOND, VA."

T26

Face Design: Hope with anchor, R. M. T. Hunter left, C. G. Memminger, right.

NOTE: There are three types of red "X" and "X" overprint. That section of the note on which the overprints appear is illustrated in double size.

Face Design: Solid red "X" and "X" overprint.

CRISWELL #	NOTE	A.B.P.	GOOD	UNC.
☐ 173-188	$10	12.00	20.00	100.00

Face Design: Coarse lace "X" and "X" red overprint.

CRISWELL #	NOTE	A.B.P.	GOOD	UNC.
☐ 189-210	$10	11.00	20.00	110.00

CONFEDERATE STATES OF AMERICA—1861 ISSUE

Face Design: Fine lace "X" and "X" red overprint.

CRISWELL #	NOTE	A.B.P.	GOOD	UNC.
☐211-220	$10	10.00	18.00	120.00

"HOYER & LUDWIG, RICHMOND, VA."

T27

Face Design: Liberty seated by shield and eagle.

CRISWELL #	NOTE	A.B.P.	GOOD	UNC.
☐221-229	$10	600.00	800.00	V.RARE

CONFEDERATE STATES OF AMERICA—1861 ISSUE

"HOYER & LUDWIG, RICHMOND, VA."

T28

Face Design: Ceres and Commerce with an urn.

CRISWELL # ☐230-234	NOTE $10	A.B.P. 2.00	GOOD 3.50	UNC. 35.00

"J. T. PATERSON, COLUMBIA, SC."

CRISWELL # ☐235-236	NOTE $10	A.B.P. 2.50	GOOD 4.75	UNC. 37.50

"B. DUNCAN, RICHMOND, VA."

T29

Face Design: Negro picking cotton.

CRISWELL # ☐237	NOTE $10	A.B.P. 12.00	GOOD 20.00	UNC. 55.00

CONFEDERATE

CONFEDERATE STATES OF AMERICA—1861 ISSUE

"B. DUNCAN, COLUMBIA, SC."

T30

Face Design: Gen. Francis Marion's "Sweet Potato Dinner." R. M. T. Hunter left, Minerva right.

CRISWELL #	NOTE	A.B.P.	GOOD	UNC.
☐238	$10	4.00	8.00	30.00

NO ENGRAVER'S NAME

CRISWELL #	NOTE	A.B.P.	GOOD	UNC.
☐239-241	$10	5.00	9.00	35.00

"SOUTHERN BANK NOTE CO., NEW ORLEANS"

T31

Face Design: Black and red on red fibre paper. Minerva left, Agriculture, Commerce, Industry, Justice and Liberty seated at center, statue of Washington right.

CRISWELL #	NOTE	A.B.P.	GOOD	UNC
☐243-245	$5	35.00	65.00	175.00

CONFEDERATE STATES OF AMERICA—1861 ISSUE

"LEGGETT, KEATINGE & BALL, RICHMOND, VA."

T32

Face Design: Black and orange red. Machinist with hammer, boy in oval left.

CRISWELL #	NOTE	A.B.P.	GOOD	UNC.
☐246-249	$5	60.00	125.00	500.00

"LEGGETT, KEATINGE & BALL, RICHMOND, VA."

T33

Face Design: Black and white note with blue green ornamentation. C.G. Memminger, Minerva right.

CRISWELL #	NOTE	A.B.P.	GOOD	UNC.
☐250-253	$5	3.75	6.50	50.00

"KEATINGE & BALL, RICHMOND, VA."

☐254-257	$5	4.75	8.00	60.00

NO ENGRAVER'S NAME

☐258-261	$5	5.50	9.00	60.00

CONFEDERATE STATES OF AMERICA—1861 ISSUE

"KEATINGE & BALL, RICHMOND, VA."

T34

Face Design: C. G. Memminger, Minerva right.

CRISWELL #	NOTE	A.B.P.	GOOD	UNC.
☐262-270	$5	8.00	12.00	50.00

"PRINTED BY HOYER & LUDWIG, RICHMOND, VA."

T35

Face Design: Loading cotton left, "Indian Princess" right.

CRISWELL #	NOTE	A.B.P.	GOOD	UNC.
☐271	$5	750.00	1500.00	V.RARE

CONFEDERATE STATES OF AMERICA—1861 ISSUE

"HOYER & LUDWIG, RICHMOND, VA."

T36

Face Design: Ceres seated on bale of cotton, sailor left.

CRISWELL #	NOTE	A.B.P.	GOOD	UNC.
☐272	$5	4.00	6.00	32.50

"J. T. PATERSON & CO., COLUMBIA, SC."

☐274	$5	4.00	5.00	30.00

"J. T. PATERSON & CO., COLUMBIA, SC."

☐276-282	$5	4.00	5.50	30.00

CONFEDERATE STATES OF AMERICA—1861 ISSUE

"B. DUNCAN, RICHMOND, VA."

T37

Face Design: Sailor seated beside bales of cotton, C.G. Memminger left, Justice and Ceres right.

CRISWELL # ☐284	NOTE $5	A.B.P. 7.00	GOOD 17.00	UNC. 45.00

"B. DUNCAN, COLUMBIA, SC."

☐285	$5	5.00	9.00	35.00

"B. DUNCAN, COLUMBIA, SC."

T38

Face Design: Personification of South striking down Union, J. P. Benjamin left.

NOTE: Dated "September 2, 1861," through an error. No Confederate note less than $5 was authorized in 1861.

CRISWELL # ☐286	NOTE $2	A.B.P. 50.00	GOOD 85.00	UNC. V.RARE

THE CONFEDERATE STATES OF AMERICA
1862

$165,000,000 Authorized by Act of "April 17th, 1862."

"HOYER & LUDWIG, RICHMOND, VA."
(Dates May 5 to May 9, 1862)

T39

Face Design: Railway train straight steam from locomotive, milkmaid left. Bears "Interest at Two Cents Per Day".

CRISWELL #	NOTE	A.B.P.	GOOD	UNC.
☐287-289	$100	6.00	12.50	25.00

"J. T. PATERSON, COLUMBIA, SC."
(Various written dates, May through October, 1862)

☐290-296	$100	6.00	10.00	15.00

T40

Face Design: Railway train diffused steam from locomotive, milkmaid left. Bears "Interest at Two Cents Per Day".

CRISWELL #	NOTE	A.B.P.	GOOD	UNC.
☐298-309	$100	6.00	10.00	15.00

CONFEDERATE STATES OF AMERICA—1862 ISSUE

"KEATINGE & BALL, COLUMBIA, SC."

NOTE: On these notes there are two types of ornamental scrolls in the upper right corners.

Scroll 1

Scroll 2

T41

Face Design: "Hundred" overprint in orange red, Bears "Interest at Two Cents Per Day". Negroes hoeing cotton, J. C. Calhoun left, Columbia right.

DATED "AUGUST 26th, 1862". (Date All Written.) Scroll No. 1.

CRISWELL #	NOTE		A.B.P.	GOOD	UNC.
☐310-314	$100		9.00	14.00	25.00

WRITTEN DATES, AUG. to DEC. "1862". ("186" of Date is Engraved.)

☐315-324	$100		8.00	12.00	15.00

DATED JANUARY 1st to JANUARY 8th, 1863.

☐325-333	$100		8.00	12.00	18.00

CONFEDERATE STATES OF AMERICA—1862 ISSUE

$5,000,000 Authorized by Act of "April 18th, 1862."
$5,000,000 Authorized by Act of "September 23rd, 1862."

"B. DUNCAN, COLUMBIA, SC."

T42

Face Design: Personification of South striking down Union. J. P. Benjamin left.

CRISWELL # ☐334-337	NOTE $2	A.B.P. 6.00	GOOD 15.00	UNC. 35.00

"B. DUNCAN, COLUMBIA, SC."

T43

Face Design: "2" and "Two" in green overprint. Personification of South striking down Union. J. P. Benjamin left.

CRISWELL # ☐338	NOTE $2	A.B.P. 10.00	GOOD 25.00	UNC. 175.00

CONFEDERATE

CONFEDERATE STATES OF AMERICA—1862 ISSUE

"B. DUNCAN, COLUMBIA, SC."

T44

Face Design: Steamship at sea, Lucy Holcombe
Pickens right, Liberty left.

CRISWELL # ☐339-341	NOTE $1	A.B.P. 4.00	GOOD 12.00	UNC. 30.00

"B. DUNCAN, COLUMBIA, SC."

T45

Face Design: Steamship at sea, Lucy Holcombe
Pickens right, Liberty Left. "1" and "One" green
overprint.

CRISWELL # ☐342	NOTE $1	A.B.P. 10.00	GOOD 30.00	UNC. 135.00

CONFEDERATE STATES OF AMERICA—1862 ISSUE

This is a Sept. 2, 1861 Note, Dated Through Error "September 2, 1862".
"HOYER & LUDWIG, RICHMOND, VA."

T46

Face Design: Ceres reclining on cotton bales, R. M. T. Hunter at Right.

NO ENGRAVERS' NAME

CRISWELL #	NOTE		A.B.P.	GOOD	UNC.
☐343-344	$10	....	6.00	10.00	60.00

"KEATINGE & BALL, COLUMBIA, SC."

Essay note, printed signatures.

T47

Face Design: Liberty seated on bale of cotton, R. M. T. Hunter right.

CRISWELL #	NOTE		A.B.P.	GOOD	UNC.
☐345	$20	....	EXTREMELY RARE		

CONFEDERATE

CONFEDERATE STATES OF AMERICA—1862 ISSUE

"KEATINGE & BALL, COLUMBIA, SC."

Essay note, printed signatures.

T48

Face Design: Ceres holding sheaf of wheat, R. M. T.
Hunter right.

CRISWELL #	NOTE	A.B.P.	GOOD	UNC.
☐346	$10		EXTREMELY RARE	

$90,000,000 Authorized by Act of "Oct. 13th, 1862."

"KEATINGE & BALL, COLUMBIA, SC."

T49

Face Design: Fancy green reverse. Lucy Holcombe
Pickens, George W. Randolph right.

CRISWELL #	NOTE	A.B.P.	GOOD	UNC.
☐347-349	$100	15.00	22.50	60.00

CONFEDERATE STATES OF AMERICA—1862 ISSUE

"KEATINGE & BALL, RICHMOND, VA."

T50

Face Design: Black and green, ornate green reverse. Portrait of Jefferson Davis.

ALL "3RD SERIES"

CRISWELL #	NOTE		A.B.P.	GOOD	UNC.
☐ 350-356	$50		7.00	12.00	40.00

"KEATINGE & BALL, COLUMBIA, SC."

☐ 357-358	$50		6.00	10.00	40.00

"KEATINGE & BALL, COLUMBIA, SC."

T51

Face Design: Fancy blue reverse. State Capitol at Nashville, Tennessee. A. H. Stephens.

CRISWELL #	NOTE		A.B.P.	GOOD	UNC.
☐ 363-368	$20		4.00	8.00	27.50

"KEATINGE & BALL, COLUMBIA, SC."
(Printed on pink paper.)

T52

Face Design: Fancy blue reverse. State Capitol at Columbia, South Carolina, R. M. T. Hunter.

"PRINTED BY B. DUNCAN, COLUMBIA, SC.""

CRISWELL # □369-375	NOTE $10	A.B.P. 2.50	GOOD 4.00	UNC. 9.00

"PRINTED BY EVANS & COGSWELL"

□376-378	$10	2.50	5.00	11.00

"ERRORS, IN THAT TWO PRINTERS' NAMES APPEAR NEXT TO EACH OTHER"

□378A-378C	$10	20.00	25.00	100.00

CONFEDERATE STATES OF AMERICA—1862 ISSUE

"KEATINGE & BALL, COLUMBIA, SC."
(Printed on pink paper.)

T53

Face Design: Fancy blue reverse. State Capitol of Richmond, Virginia. C. G. Memminger.

NOTE: There are many varieties of printers names on notes of this issue, though all have the same engraver's names. In general the only valuable ones are those with two "printers" names.

CRISWELL # □379-390	NOTE $5	A.B.P. 2.50	GOOD 3.50	UNC. 9.00

"KEATINGE & BALL, COLUMBIA, SC."
(Printed on pink paper.)

T54

Face Design: Portrait of Judah P. Benjamin.

CRISWELL # □391-395	NOTE $2	A.B.P. 3.50	GOOD 7.00	UNC. 35.00

"PRINTED BY J. T. PATERSON & CO."

□396	$2		3.00	5.00	32.50

CONFEDERATE

CONFEDERATE STATES OF AMERICA—1862 ISSUE

"KEATINGE & BALL, COLUMBIA, SC."
(Printed on pink paper.)

T55

Face Design: Portrait of Clement C. Clay.

CRISWELL # ☐397-400	NOTE $1	A.B.P. 4.00	GOOD 9.00	UNC. 30.00

"PRINTED BY B. DUNCAN, COLUMBIA, SC."
(No series. Script serial letter.)

☐401	$1	5.00	10.00	35.00

Col. Grover C. Criswell

Known as the *"Richest Man in the World in Confederate Money"*, has been a Collector-Dealer for 35 years.

He has authored numerous books and articles on Confederate Currency, lectured extensively on the subject, had articles published and illustrated in *Parade Magazine, Life Magazine, People Magazine* and many hobby publications. He has appeared on such National T.V. Shows as *"What's My Line", "To Tell The Truth"* and *"The Today Program"*.

A Life Member of the American Numismatic Association, he has served seven terms as a member of the Board of Governors, and President.

He is a member of over 100 Numismatic, Philatelic and Historical Societies, 60 of which are life memberships and served on the Florida Civil War Centennial Commission and as an advisor to the National Civil War Centennial Commission.

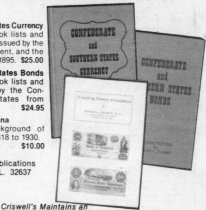